CW00922756

Schrodinger's Equation

Applications to Simple

Physical Systems

Lectures by

George E. Parris

Copyright December 2015

Paperback 2021

Forward

I have finally gotten around to putting this document in paperback form. Over the last 6 years, it has actually been one of the most downloaded digital documents of my library.

It is my experience that most of the chemist teaching chemistry today and the those that write the textbooks they use really do not know much about how Edwin Schrodinger's equation works. There is lots of "professorial handwaving" in most classes when the topics of *wavefunctions* and *entropy* come up and I have been trying to fix that.

I hope this helps.

George E Parris Ph.D.
February 18, 2021

1.0 History and Introduction

The existence of atoms and molecules was an arguable topic among physicists into the first few years of the 1900s. If Albert Einstein (1879-1955) had published nothing else, his work on Brownian motion (1905) and its implication of the existence of atoms and molecules would have been important. Ironically, without relying on physics or any known theory of atoms or chemical bonding, organic chemists had deduced that organic molecules composed of atoms existed and that these atoms were fixed in very specific structures relative to one another by inert bonds. The theory of structural chemistry established by Jacobus Henricus van 't Hoff, Jr. (1852-1911) in 1884 was brutally criticized by the leading (organic) chemist of the day Hermann Kolbe (1818-1884) before its predictive power was demonstrated by Emil Fischer (1852-1919) who used it to explain the optical active isomers of simple carbohydrates between 1888 and 1894. Kolbe and the physics of his day were only aware of one force that might hold molecules together and that was electrostatic attraction, which did not require any specific interatomic geometry and did not require inert[1] bonding. Nonetheless, organic chemists

---

[1] *Inert* means "changes only slowly," while *stable* means a "free energy minimum."

plunged ahead into the 1900s with a firm belief in atoms joined into molecules by directional bonds. For the most part, the physicists were oblivious to these notions.

The faith of the organic chemists was rewarded by the x-ray crystallography of hexamethylbenzene by Kathleen Lonsdale in 1929. The carbons of the molecule were all in same plane and arranged in a hexagonal with equal distances between the carbons in the benzene ring. This is not what electrostatics would predict.

https://godandnature.asa3.org/uploads/2/4/7/3/2473392/6170856.jpg

1.1 The Nuclear Atom

Using a highly evacuated electric discharge tube, J. J. Thomson (1856-1940) discovered the electron in 1897. There had been various speculative estimates of the size and mass of atoms and Thomson could apply physics to determine the ratio of mass to charge of the electron (m/e). However, it was obvious that the mass of the electron (assigned a negative charge (-)) was far less than the positively charged part of the atom. The physicists also had no clue as to the number of electrons in an individual atom. Given the electrons relatively small mass, there might be thousands (which implied that there might be thousands of positive charges in an atom.

Thus, in 1904, Thomson dared to propose a physical model of the atom based on electrostatics. He assumed that the positive charge of the atom was a single contiguous mass and that the electrons were embedded in this positive charge (the so-called plume pudding model). As much as this model is often derided in classrooms today, the point should be made that Thomson was building on the known facts of his day.[2]

But the times, they were a changing.

As an aside, work by Wilhelm Conrad Röntgen (1845-1923) using similar equipment (but studying different phenomena), revealed the x-rays (November 1895). Within a few months (March 1896), Henri Becquerel (1852-1908) discovered similar rays produced without the aid of

---

[2] The same is true for Kolbe's attack on structural chemistry.

cathode rays (high energy electrons). These observations led his student Marie Skłodowska-Curie and her husband to attempt to isolate the source form natural minerals. This turned out to be a much bigger job than they expected. This work contributed to the understanding of the nature of what would be called "the nucleus" of the atom, but it is not relevant to our current story.

Thomson's student Ernest Rutherford (1871-1937) had initially been interested in electromagnetic radiation; but when bested by Guglielmo Marconi (1874-1937), Rutherford turned to study of the radioactive phenomenon being pursued by the Curie's. With collaborator Frederick Soddy, the young professor established a reputation in understanding radiation and the particles that were released by atoms. Rutherford became particularly interested in the positively charged mass, he named the alpha particle.

Meanwhile, Robert Millikan (who was skeptical of the work of Thomson and pretty much everyone else) set out to prove him wrong, but ironically determined the charge on an electron (1.59×10^{-19} Coulomb) between 1908 and 1917.

Rutherford was building up a top research group going into World War I and acquired post-doc Hans Geiger and graduate student Ernest Marsden. Perhaps in response to

Millikan's skepticism, Rutherford set Geiger and Marsden the task of studying the penetration of gold foils by alpha particles in a series of experiments conducted between 1908 and 1909. Based on the Thomson model of the atom, they expected to see some uniform attenuation of the particles, but through their diligent work, they noticed that about one in a thousand of the alphas was deflected at great angles, while most went straight through with minimal attenuation. Rutherford allowed his post-doc and student (Geiger-Marsden) to publish their experimental results, but declined to have them speculate on the interpretation of the results. After about a year (in 1911)[3], he (alone) published an article based on their observations and his calculations that described a *nuclear atom*: The positive charge and almost all the mass is concentrated in a tiny volume and most of the volume of the atom occupied by the electrons.

This model flew in the face of everything known of classical electrostatic theory: How can the negative change and positive charge be separated from one another? The first though was that the nuclear atom might be a planetary system (centripetal force balancing electrostatic attraction).

---

[3] E. Rutherford, The Scattering of α and β Particles by Matter and the Structure of the Atom, *Philosophical Magazine*. Series 6, vol. 21. May 1911.

1.2 Atomic Spectra

Meanwhile, there was a body of data (atomic spectra) that had defied explanation of nearly 100 years. Light had been accepted to have wave properties very early (1700s) and the prism had allowed white light to be resolved into various wavelengths. It was then shown that various wavelengths could be recombined to form different colors without changing the wavelengths. For example, a beam of blue light could be crossed with a beam of yellow light and where they crossed there was a green color; but the blue beam and yellow beam emerged from the mixed zone unchanged. Color is a perception of the eye; not an intrinsic property of light.

The association of specific color and then specific line spectra with each element was an interesting phenomenon with practical application in analytical chemistry. The presence and even the relative quantities of elements in a sample could be determined in seconds with a crude spectrometer; avoiding hours of wet chemistry separations and precipitations. Indeed, new elements could be discovered this way. Robert Bunsen (1811–1899) and Gustav Kirchhoff (1824–1887) made use of a metal-free hydrocarbon flame (produced by a Bunsen burner) to discover cesium and rubidium in 1860.

Johannes Rydberg (1854-1919) was a Swedish physicist, who observed the spectra of the numerous alkali metals found in his country, assumed that the patterns of lines he observed were caused by some underlying physical principle and attempted to make sense of the spectra. He was not making much progress; he could not find a simple mathematical formula that organized the data. Meanwhile in Switzerland, a young physicist suggested the problem to the aging mathematician Johann Jakob Balmer (1825-1898). Balmer only had one atomic spectrum with which to work; but it was a simple one, hydrogen.

Spectrum by Jan Homann, source Wikimedia Commons

Without much effort, he found a relationship that was consistent with all the readily visible lines (i.e., the Balmer series, 1885):

$$\lambda = B\left(\frac{n^2}{n^2 - m^2}\right) = B\left(\frac{n^2}{n^2 - 2^2}\right)$$

Where B is a constant and m = 2 and n = 3, 4, 5, etc.

The remarkable thing was that using this equation he predicted other fainter lines and lines that were not in the visible spectrum (longer and shorter wavelength) which were soon observed. Predictive power is always a good sign in science.

Rydberg soon heard of these breakthroughs and quickly reformulated Balmer's equation (for hydrogen and "hydrogen-like" elements)[4]:

$$\frac{1}{\lambda_{\text{vac}}} = R \left(\frac{1}{n_1^2} - \frac{1}{n_2^2} \right)$$

Then he incorporated additional terms in the equation (1890) to account for the irregularities seen in his alkali metal spectra.[5]

---

[4] The term "hydrogen-like" atom means that there is a nucleus with a positive charge that is equal to the atomic number (z), but **only one electron**. The complications that had frustrated Rydberg to that point was the interactions (mutual repulsions) of the electrons.

[5] The higher order terms performed the same function as additional quantum numbers (l and m_l).

1.3 Planck's Postulate

Max Planck (1858-1947) began trying to explain "blackbody" (continuum)[6] radiation in 1894 in an effort to maximize the light from the recently invented light bulb while using the least energy. After several frustrating and failed attempts to derive a mathematical relation that predicted the observed continuum spectrum with classical thermodynamics, he reluctantly adopted a concept proposed in 1877 by Ludwig Boltzmann (1844-1906). In this model, energy associated with all sorts of physical processes were restricted to unique increments (a x n, where n = 1, 2, 3…) called *energy levels*. This idea was contrary to our normal experience and not based on any known fundamental law. With this assumption, Planck could make his derivation work. Thus, in December 1900, he proposed that light was quantized (delivered in packets of energy called *photons*) and that the energy of a photon was given by the following equation:

$$E_{photon} = nh\nu = nhc\,(1/\lambda)$$

---

[6] All surfaces give off a continuum of thermal radiation. The spectrum is related to the surface temperature. Conservation of energy and momentum as atoms randomly collide requires release of electromagnetic radiation.

Where n = 1, 2, 3…,

v is the frequency of light;

λ is the corresponding wavelength;

c is the speed of light; and

h is a constant (Planck's constant).

Of course, Planck and all physicists were skeptical of this seemingly arbitrary restriction on energy. Moreover, how could a wave disperse and yet yield a concentrated packet of energy wherever it was absorbed.

During this same timeframe, Heinrich Hertz (1857-1894) observed in 1887 that electrodes produced sparks more easily when a short-wavelength light was shown upon them (i.e., the *photoelectric effect*). Albert Einstein gave Planck's postulate a boost in 1905 when he published a paper proposing that it would explain the photoelectric effect. Specifically, he argued that the photons were absorbed by the electrode and excited electrons by the discrete amount:

$$\Delta E = h\nu$$

But, when the energy of excitation (ΔE) was not enough to overcome the energy needed to rip the electron from the metal (atoms); there was no enhanced current (i.e., spark between electrodes). But, when the energy of the photons reached a certain level, the corresponding energy of excitation was enough to facilitate the ionization of the electron from the surface of the electrode.

Planck was, of course, very pleased to see his idea applied to another problem, although the young Einstein[7] had little academic standing and did not actually do any experiments. The experimental confirmation of the photoelectric effect was actually taken up by (skeptical) Robert A. Millikan who proved it in 1914 and made an accurate determination of Planck's constant (6.626×10^{-34} J-s). Millikan remained skeptical of Einstein's interpretation, which seems to have been his nature. Perhaps skepticism is what made him a magnificent experimentalist.

1.4 The Bohr Atomic Model

Neils Bohr (1885-1962) briefly worked for Rutherford (1911) in England and subsequently communicated with Rutherford about the nuclear model of the atom in some detail. The problem as noted above was explaining how the negative electrons were held apart from the positively charged nucleus. Back home in Denmark, in 1913, Bohr

---

[7] This probably explains Planck's support for Einstein throughout his career.

welded the Rydberg equation of atomic spectra and the
Planck postulate as applied by Einstein to the structure of
the atom as developed by Rutherford on top of the
experiments of Geiger and Marsden. The result was a
planetary model:

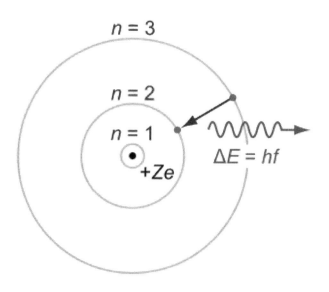

Drawing by JabberWok, source Wikimedia Commons

Today, the actual logic used by Bohr appears to be tortured
and indirect. A semi-classical analysis quickly derives the
empirical Rydberg constant in readily identifiable units:

$$R_\infty = \frac{m_e e^4}{8\varepsilon_0^2 h^3 c} = 1.097\ 373\ 156\ 8539(55) \times 10^7\ \text{m}^{-1},$$

The atomic spectra (absorption and emissions) were explained by electronic transitions among allowed energy levels ($\Delta E = E_{final} - E_{initial}$). And, the energy of an energy level was defined as:

$$E_n = -\frac{Z^2 R_E}{n^2}$$

1.5 The Degrees of Freedom of an Electron

World War I (1914-1918) diverted the scientific and engineering efforts of nearly everyone in Europe and, indeed, took the lives of several scientists who were pushing forward the frontiers of this research. Even Marie Curie and her daughter worked as x-ray technicians for the French while Lisa Meitner did similar work for the Germans. After the war, it took a time for scientists to begin focusing on atomic theory again.

Wolfgang Pauli (1900-1956) was working on the problem of explaining the stability of the Bohr atom and took a classical thermodynamics approach recognizing that the electron must have three degrees of freedom for its movement in three-dimensional space. But, with three-degrees of freedom he still could not explain the atomic spectra of multi-electron atoms. However, he noted that if he included a fourth degree of freedom inherent to the electron (later identified as the electron magnetic moment, "spin") he could make the model fit the data (1924). These four degrees of freedom are the parameters needed to define an electron in space and we will see them more clearly identified in the work of Heisenberg and Schrodinger (below). Out of this work, came support for the idea that electrons appear in pairs. The idea of electron pairs had been offered by chemist Gilbert N. Lewis (1875-1946) in his 1916 paper "Atoms and Molecules."[8]

1.6 Stable Discrete Bohr Orbits

Since the time of H. Hertz and through the study of x-rays and gamma-rays there had been an ongoing debate about particles and waves especially as they are diffracted in a double-slit experiment. The paradox is how can a wave be dispersed in space and yet produce a discrete energy

---

[8] Gilbert N. Lewis. Atoms and molecules. J. Am. Chem. Soc. 38(4):762-865 (1916).

change associated will all its energy at a specific point.[9]

This paradox had continued and was expanded as a general phenomenon of all particles (even macroscopic particles) by Louis de Broglie (1892–1987)[10] who described his 1924 thesis as follows:

> "The fact that, following Einstein's introduction of photons in light waves, one knew that light contains particles which are concentrations of energy incorporated into the wave, suggests that all particles, like the electron, must be transported by a wave into which it is incorporated... My essential idea was to extend to all particles the coexistence of waves and particles discovered by Einstein in 1905 in the case of light and photons."

In his remarkable thesis, he postulated the equivalence of waves and matter based on Einstein's equation and Planck's postulate:

$$mc^2 = E = h\nu = hc(1/\lambda)$$

$$mc = h(1/\lambda)$$

$$\lambda = h/mc$$

---

[9] See for example the discussion by W.H. Bragg, Barkla and von Laue earlier in this chapter.

[10] A student of Paul Langevin at the Sorbonne in Paris.

Where mc = momentum = p

For particles not moving at the speed of light (c) the equation becomes:

$$\lambda = \frac{h}{p} = \frac{h}{mv}\sqrt{1 - \frac{v^2}{c^2}}$$

Obviously, electrons (very light particles with mass = m) could thus be represented as waves and the corresponding wavelength (λ) would be comparable to the size of an atom.[11] Thus, de Broglie could suppose that the observed (stable and discrete) energy levels of Bohr's model required that the electron wave be a *standing wave* and the simplest idea (in two dimensions) was that the Bohr orbitals were sinusoidal paths in which only an even number of wavelengths could be stable.

---

[11] This hypothesis was proven in 1927 by C. J. Davisson (1881 - 1958) and L. H. Germer (1896 - 1971) by observing electron diffraction on a crystal of nickel atoms.

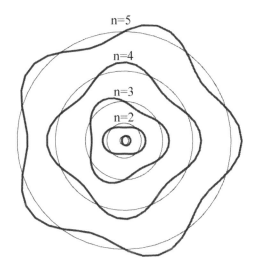

http://skullsinthestars.com/2015/05/20/1975-the-year-that-quantum-mechanics-met-gravity/

Under de Broglie's principle, this is equivalent to saying that allowed orbits of the electron particles must be consistent with constructive interference of the electron waves.

1.7 Heisenberg Matrix Mechanics (1925-26)

Warner Heisenberg (1901-1976) studied mathematics and physics as a student of Arnold Somerfield in Munich. There he was also educated by Wilhelm Wien. And, he was a contemporary of Wolfgang Pauli who was also a student of Somerfield. Heisenberg (1923) followed Pauli (1921) to Göttingen where he studied under Max Born (1882-1970).

There he grappled with the rationalization of the Bohr Model. His reasoning is very baroque and requires more mathematics than available to most physicists. Nonetheless, through collaboration with Pauli and Born he developed a description of the energy states of an atom using matrices (1925-1926).

Fortunately for chemists, Heisenberg's abstract presentation was quickly replaced by a system that is more intuitively apparent to chemists.

1.7 Schrodinger's Wave Mechanics

Erwin Schrodinger (1887-1961) saw the limitations of attempts by Bohr and de Broglie to describe the atom (see below) during the period 1900-1925. In particular, Schrodinger was inclined to view the electron as a wave; and he felt that he could derive a model of the atom exclusively from the position of interpreting the electron as a wave. Thus, he invented a technique of analysis that leads to a series of quantum numbers to describe the energy of the electron in space, with some parallel to the classical degrees of freedom considered by Pauli. This work was published in 1926.

Few chemists understand the mathematics involved in the solution of the problem and as a rule, chemistry courses teach only the results of the calculations and present them with little or no real rationale. Schrodinger was familiar with a type of mathematical equation known (in German) as "eigenvalue[12]" equations.

Before advancing to discuss the atom (below), it is worthwhile to show how Schrodinger approached some simple problems and solved his equation. It is relevant that the mathematical form of the equation cannot be solved analytically except for simple problems and when applied to atoms more complex than hydrogen, approximation methods are required to obtain useful results. When applied to the hydrogen atom problem, the Schrodinger equation produces a series of wave functions that give rise to three-dimensional probability distributions (called orbitals[13]) for electrons with certain quantum numbers.

The Schrodinger Equation is typically represented in the eigen function format:

---

[12] This translates into English as "characteristic value." But most chemists are so baffled by the concept that they have adopted the German-based term. (Since they do not understand the mathematics, they are afraid to change the terminology and possibly mis-representing it.)

[13] Bohr had used the analogy of the atom to the solar system and described the electrons as moving in circular *orbits*. The orbitals are standing (time-independent) waves.

$$\hat{H}\,\Psi = E\Psi$$

Here "$\hat{H}$" is a mathematical operator for energy called the Hamiltonian operator. "E" strands for energy and "Ψ" stands for the wave function that represents the electron.

The Hamiltonian operator addresses both the kinetic energy and the potential energy of the electron in three-dimensional space and can be written as

$H_{operator}$ = kinetic energy operator

+ potential energy operator

$H_{operator}$ = $\hat{H}$ = - [$\hbar^2$ / 2m] $\blacktriangledown^2$ + V(x,y,z)

Where $\hbar$ = h/2π and

"$\blacktriangledown^2$" is shorthand for the three second-order partial derivatives:

$$\blacktriangledown^2 = \partial^2 / \partial x^2 + \partial^2 / \partial y^2 + \partial^2 / \partial z^2$$

In the following paragraphs, the Schrodinger Equation will be applied to progressively more challenging problems:

2.0   Examples

The Schrodinger equation is generally presented to first-year students with no attempt to solve it or even explain what the symbols mean. Very few chemists or physicists ever actually solve real problems with its application. But it is useful to apply the principle to simple systems as a demonstration of the technique. Here I have summarized three cases that I have come across in my career from lectures given in the 1960s by professors at NC State University and Georgia Tech.

2.1 Quantum States of a Free Electron

A "free electron" moves through space and is not affected by any potential field. Thus, we can immediately simplify the Hamiltonian operator by realizing that the potential energy $V(x,y,z) = 0$. Without loss of rigor, we can also avoid voluminous mathematical operations by choosing the x-axis of our coordinate system to coincide with the direction of travel of the electron such that $\blacktriangledown^2$ reduces to $\blacktriangledown^2 = \partial^2/\partial x^2$. Thus, for a free electron, Schrodinger's Equation reduces to

$$- [\hbar^2 / 2m] (\partial^2 \Psi / \partial x^2) = E \Psi$$

This equation can be immediately rearranged to

$$[\hbar^2 / 2m] (\partial^2 \Psi / \partial x^2) + E \Psi = 0$$

We will use the shorthand Ψ'' to stand for $(\partial^2 \Psi / \partial x^2)$

$$[\hbar^2 / 2m] \Psi'' + E \Psi = 0$$

or

$$\Psi'' + [2m E / \hbar^2] \Psi = 0 \qquad \textit{(Equation 1)}$$

Equations of this form can be solved analytically if

$$\Psi = e^{\alpha x} \text{ such that}$$

$$\Psi' = \alpha e^{\alpha x} \text{ and } \Psi'' = \alpha^2 e^{\alpha x}$$

Substituting these exponential forms for Ψ'' and Ψ

into *Equation 1* yields:

$$\alpha^2 e^{\alpha x} + [2m E / \hbar^2] e^{\alpha x} = 0$$

Factoring gives us

$$e^{\alpha x} (\alpha^2 + [2m\,E\,/\,\hbar^2]) = 0$$

the term $e^{\alpha x}$ cannot be "zero" if α and x are positive or finite, thus the other term must be zero:

$$\alpha^2 + [2m\,E\,/\,\hbar^2] = 0$$

from which we can solve for α

$$\alpha = \pm\,i\,(2mE\,/\,\hbar^2)^{1/2} = \pm\,i\,(2mE)^{1/2}\,/\,\hbar$$

Substituting this expression back into our equation for Ψ

$$\Psi = e^{\alpha x} = e^{\pm\,i\,[(2mE)^{1/2}/\hbar]\,x}$$

This exponential is mathematically equivalent to the following expression:

$$\Psi = A \cos [(2mE)^{1/2}\,/\,\hbar]\,x \; + B \sin [(2mE)^{1/2}\,/\,\hbar]\,x$$

(Equation 2)

The only requirements for Ψ are that it be real and finite. Thus, E (the energy) can take on *any real, positive value* because for any real positive value of E, Ψ will be finite and real. Moreover, the electron is represented by a sinusoidal wave along the x-axis.

Thus, we can conclude that a free electron can take on kinetic energy states that are not quantized. By analogy, electromagnetic radiation can take on any energy (a continuum spectrum).

2.2 An Electron in a One-Dimensional Potential Well

We can apply an approach similar to that used above to investigate other situations. One of the classic problems assumes that the electron is trapped in an "infinite square potential well" (i.e., the particle in a box).

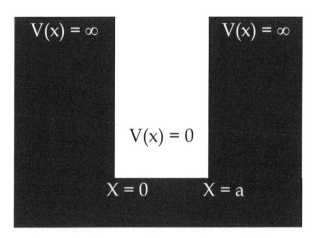

Inside the well, the particle (electron) has no potential energy. Outside the box, the particle would have infinite potential energy (hence the particle cannot escape from the box). Again, we begin with the Schrodinger Equation and the energy operator:

$$\hat{H}\,\Psi = E\Psi$$

$$\hat{H} = - [\hbar^2/\,2m]\,\nabla^2 + V(x,y,z)$$

And again, we will limit ourselves to one dimension such that

$$\nabla^2 = \partial^2/\partial x^2$$

Then,

$$- [\hbar^2/\,2m]\,(\partial^2\,\Psi/\partial x^2) + V(x)\,\Psi = E\,\Psi$$

which can be rearranged to

$$[\hbar^2/\,2m]\,(\partial^2\,\Psi/\partial x^2) + (E - V(x))\,\Psi = 0$$

Consider what happens outside the box ($x \leq 0$ or $x \geq a$):

$$[\hbar^2/\,2m]\,(\partial^2\,\Psi/\partial x^2) + (E - \infty)\,\Psi = 0$$

and thus,

$$\Psi \text{ must} = 0 \quad \text{for } x \leq 0 \text{ or } x \geq a$$

However, if we consider the region $0 < x < a$, where $V(x) = 0$, we can write

$$\Psi'' + [2m\,E\,/\,\hbar^2]\,\Psi = 0 \qquad (Equation\ 1)$$

just as in the case of the free electron problem. Applying the same strategy for solution as in the free electron problem (above), we derive

$$\Psi = A\,\cos\,[(2mE\,)^{1/2}\,/\,\hbar]\,x\ + B\,\sin\,[(2mE\,)^{1/2}\,/\,\hbar]\,x$$

$$(Equation\ 2)$$

However, unlike the free electron problem (above), we must place boundary conditions on *Equation 2* for the electron trapped in the potential well. Specifically, for Ψ to be continuous everywhere, it must be zero at $x = 0$ and $x = a$. These conditions allow us to solve for the coefficients A and B in *Equation 2*.

$$\Psi = 0 = A\,\cos\,[(2mE\,)^{1/2}\,/\,\hbar]\,0\ + B\,\sin\,[(2mE\,)^{1/2}\,/\,\hbar]\,0$$

Note that $\sin 0 = 0$ and $\cos 0 = 1$

Thus, $0 = A$ and Equation 2 becomes

$$\Psi = B \sin [(2mE)^{1/2}/\hbar] \, x$$

Which must be evaluated at x = a

$$\Psi = 0 = B \sin [(2mE)^{1/2}/\hbar] \, a$$

Obviously, B might = 0, but that would be trivial (*i.e.*, if the wave function were zero everywhere, the conditions would be met). However, in order for this equation to be true with a *non-zero value of B*, then

$$[(2mE)^{1/2}/\hbar] \, a \ \ \text{must} = n\,\pi$$

Since **m** and **ħ** and **a** are all constants, *E can only take on certain discrete values to achieve this result.*

The system is quantized!

We can set **a** arbitrarily at a value of 1, then rearranging this equation,

$$E_n = (n^2\, \pi^2\, \hbar^2)/2m = (n^2 h^2)/8m$$

Remember that $\hbar = h/2\pi$

Thus, the allowable energies are discrete units with n = 1, 2, 3, …

and we can write

$$\Psi = B \sin [(2mE_n)^{1/2} / \hbar] x$$

This is the wave function, but we have not assigned a value to **B**.

It is customary to normalize the wave function such that the product of Ψ and its complex conjugate Ψ^* integrated over all space is equal to 1 (unity). That is, the probability of finding the electron somewhere in space is exactly equal to unity. Thus,

$$\int_{-\infty}^{+\infty} \Psi\Psi^* \, d\tau = 1 = \int_{0}^{a} B^2 \sin^2[(2mE_n)^{1/2} / \hbar] x$$

Remember the trigonometric identity:
$$\sin^2 \Theta = \tfrac{1}{2}(1 - \cos 2\Theta)$$

thus,

$$2/B^2 = \int_0^a (1 - \cos 2[(2mE_n)^{1/2}/\hbar] x)\, dx$$

which can be integrated,

$$2/B^2 = x - (\sin 2\,[(2mE_n)^{1/2}/\hbar]\, x)\;[(2mE_n)^{1/2}/\hbar]^{-1}$$

and the second term is always going to be zero for allowed values of E_n.

Thus,

$$2/B^2 = a \text{ which yields } B = (2/a)^{1/2}$$

Finally, the normalized wave function for an electron in an infinite square potential well ($0 < x < a$) is

$$\Psi(n) = (2/a)^{1/2}\, \sin\,[(2mE_n)^{1/2}/\hbar]\, x$$

2.3 An Electron in a Three-Dimensional Well

Consider a three-dimensional coordinate system and a potential box with dimensions
$$x = a, y = b, z = c.$$

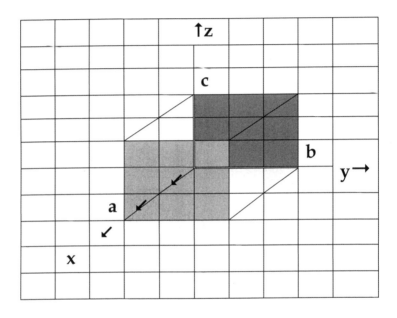

$$\hat{H}\,\Psi(x,y,z) = E\Psi(x,y,z)$$

$$\hat{H} = -\,[\hbar^2/\,2m]\,\blacktriangledown^2 + V(x,y,z)$$

Where, inside the box $V(x,y,z) = 0$ and outside the box $V(x,y,z) = \infty$

Thus, inside the box

$$\hat{H} = -[\hbar^2/2m]\;\nabla^2 = -[\hbar^2/2m]\;(\partial^2/\partial x^2 + \partial^2/\partial y^2 + \partial^2/\partial z^2)$$

Then,

$$-[\hbar^2/2m]\;(\partial^2\Psi/\partial x^2 + \partial^2\Psi/\partial y^2 + \partial^2\Psi/\partial z^2) = E\,\Psi$$

which can be rearranged to

$$\partial^2\Psi/\partial x^2 + \partial^2\Psi/\partial y^2 + \partial^2\Psi/\partial z^2 + (2mE/\hbar)\,\Psi = 0$$

and assume that the three-dimensional wave function Ψ is the product of each of the one-dimensional elements:

$$\Psi(x,y,z) = X(x)Y(y)Z(z)$$

Thus

$$\partial^2\,X(x)Y(y)Z(z)/\partial x^2 + \partial^2\,X(x)Y(y)Z(z)/\partial y^2 +$$
$$\partial^2 X(x)Y(y)Z(z)/\partial z^2 + (2mE/\hbar)\,X(x)Y(y)Z(z) = 0$$

Thus

$$X''(x)/X(x) + Y''(y)/Y(y) + Z''(z)/Z(z) + (2mE/\hbar) = 0$$

Which can be rearranged to

$$X''(x)/X(x) + Y''(y)/Y(y) + (2mE/\hbar) = -Z''(z)/Z(z)$$

In any one-dimensional line along the z-axis
$$0 = X''(x)/X(x) = Y''(y)/Y(y)$$

Thus, we can solve the equation by considering it to be three one-dimensional problems

$$(2mE/\hbar) = -Z''(z)/Z(z)$$

or
$$Z''(z) + (2mE/\hbar)\, Z(z) = 0 \quad \textit{(Equation 1 for one dimension}$$

as seen in the one-dimensional box problem (above) this type of equation yields solutions of the following type:

$$Z(z) = (2/c)^{1/2} \sin\left((2mEn_z)^{1/2}/\hbar\right) z$$
$$\text{and}$$
$$En_z = (n_z\,\hbar\,\pi/\,z)^2/2m$$

Given the Postulate:

If $\hat{H} = \Sigma_i \hat{H}(q_i)$ and $\Psi = \Pi_i \Psi(q_i)$, then $E_{tot} = \Sigma_i E(q_i)$

We can now write:

$\Psi(x,y,z) = (2/a)^{1/2} (2/b)^{1/2} (2/c)^{1/2}$
$$X [\sin (2mEn_x)^{1/2}/ \hbar) x]$$
$$[\sin (2mEn_y)^{1/2}/ \hbar) y]$$
$$[\sin (2mEn_z)^{1/2}/ \hbar) z]$$

and

$E_{tot} = - [(\hbar \pi)^2/ 2m] [(n_x/a)^2 + (n_y/b)^2 + (n_z/c)^2]$

Where all the quantum numbers (n_i) are positive integers.

2.4 Particle in a
One-Dimensional Space
Constrained by a
Harmonic Oscillator Potential Function

The harmonic oscillator function is relevant to molecular vibrations and infers a parabolic potential well:

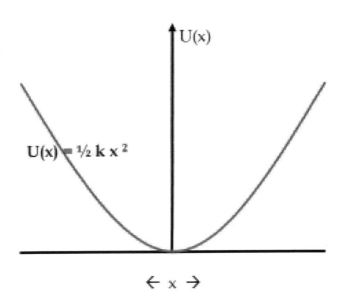

Unlike the square potential well (discussed above) the particle may be anywhere along the x-axis. In this derivation, we want to find an expression for the energy (E) of the system. After that, we will determine the normalization constant (A) that ensures that the probability of finding the particle somewhere in the x dimension is exactly equal to unity.

The energy expression can be derived as follows:

$$\text{Kinetic Energy Operator} = (-h^2/8\pi^2 m)\, \partial^2/dx^2$$

$$\text{Potential Energy Operator} = U(x) = \tfrac{1}{2}\, k\, x^2$$

Applying Schrodinger's equation:

$$KE_{op}\,\Psi + PE_{op}\,\Psi = E\,\Psi$$

$$(-h^2/8\pi^2 m)\, \partial^2\Psi/dx^2 + \Psi\,(\tfrac{1}{2}\,k\,x^2) = E\,\Psi \qquad \textit{(equation 1)}$$

Which rearranges to

$$(-h^2/8\pi^2 m)\, \partial^2\Psi/dx^2 + \Psi\,(\tfrac{1}{2}\,k\,x^2 - E) = 0$$

Which we note is in the form of

$$\Psi'' + (x^2 - A)\,\Psi = 0$$

This form yields solutions of the form

$$\Psi = A\ e^{-ax^2}$$

where "A" is the normalization constant for the wave function

$$\Psi' = A\ (-ax^2)e^{-ax^2}$$

$$\Psi'' = -2aA\ [e^{-ax^2} + (-2ax^2)\ e^{-ax^2}] = A\ e^{-ax^2}\ [-2a + 4a^2x^2]$$

and the magnitude of the wave function is a function of x.

Substituting the expressions for forms Ψ and Ψ'' into *equation 1* (above)

$$(-h^2/8\pi^2 m)\ [A\ e^{-ax^2}\ [-2a + 4a^2x^2]] + (\tfrac{1}{2}\ k\ x^2)\ [A\ e^{-ax^2}] =$$
$$E\ [A\ e^{-ax^2}]$$

Which simplifies as follows:

$$(-h^2/8\pi^2 m)\ (-2a) + [(-h^2/8\pi^2 m)\ (4a^2x^2) + (\tfrac{1}{2}\ k\ x^2)] = E$$

and

$$(h^2a/4\pi^2 m) + [(\tfrac{1}{2}\ k) - (h^2a^2/2\pi^2 m)]\ x^2 = E$$

n the general solution shown above, E is a function of x
i.e., the position of the particle). This is not consistent with
a *discrete energy level* where the energy is constant regardless
of the position of the particle. However, the energy of the
system will be constant if the term in brackets equals zero:

$$[(½\, k) - (h^2a^2/2\pi^2m)] = 0$$

This allows us to solve for "a"

$$(½\, k) = (h^2a^2/2\pi^2m)$$

Simplifying

$$k = h^2a^2/\pi^2m$$

Thus

$$a = (\pi/h)(km)^{½}$$

When the term in brackets equals zero, we can write:

$$(h^2a/4\pi^2m) = E$$

and substitute for "a"

$$(h^2/4\pi^2m)\,(\pi/h)(Km)^{½} = E$$

Which simplifies to

$$(h/4\pi)\ (K/m)^{1/2}\ =\ (\tfrac{1}{2}\,h)\ (1/2\pi)\ (K/m)^{1/2}\ =\ E$$

We know that the first energy level must be: $\tfrac{1}{2}\,h\,\nu = E$ so we can write

$$\nu = (1/2\pi)\ (k/m)^{1/2}$$

(this is the well-known equation for the frequency (ν) of a harmonic oscillator)

And the entire set of energy levels will be given by

$$(\tfrac{1}{2} + n)\ h\,\nu = E$$

$$\text{where } n = 0, 1, 2, 3, 4, \dots$$

We can evaluate the normalization constant (A) as follows:

$$1 = \int_{-\infty}^{+\infty} \Psi^2\, dx \ = \ \int_{-\infty}^{+\infty} A^2 e^{-2ax^2}\, dx$$

Thus,

$$A = \left[1/ \int e^{-2ax^2}\, dx\right]^{1/2}$$

t follows that

$$\Psi^2 = (e^{-2ax^2}) [1/\int e^{-2ax^2} dx] = (e^{-2ax^2})/\int e^{-2ax^2} dx$$

This is the equation for the well-known normal distribution bell-shaped curve), which shows the probability of finding he particle along the x-axis.

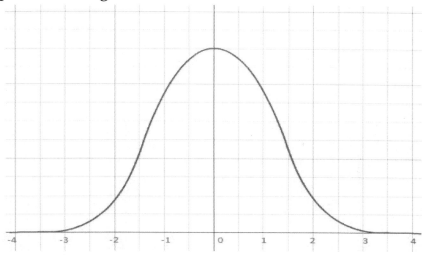

ource: http://images.tutorvista.com/cms/images/113/normal-istribution-curve.png

3.0 Linus Pauling and the Chemists

Schrodinger's approach thrilled the atomic physicists and had the advantage that it provided wave functions predicting the probability of finding the electron that could be visualized in three-dimensions. But, for nearly 40 years, the (organic) chemists had been convinced that atoms were bound together in molecules with well-established three-dimensional shapes...*and none of them were accounted for by Schrodinger's <u>atomic</u> wave functions.*

3.1 Lewis and Langmuir view the Bohr Model

Following the contributions of Rutherford in 1911, Thompson in 1912 and Bohr in 1913, G.N. Lewis published his ideas on valence and bonding in 1916 as "*The Atom and the Molecule,*"[14] which clarified the nature of the covalent bond as shared valence electrons. Soon thereafter, Irving Langmuir (1881–1957) who wrote a paper entitled "*The*

---

[14] G.N. Lewis. The atom and the molecule. *J. Am. Chem. Soc.*, 1916, 38 (4), pp 762–785.

Arrangement of Electrons in Atoms and Molecules" in 1919[15] popularized the idea that there must be concentric layers of electrons in atoms to account for the non-valence electrons, i.e., "concentric theory of atomic structure." This idea was not new in the sense that Thomson and Nagaoka had envisioned a body of swirling electrons around a central mass of positive charge. But, with the nuclear model now firmly entrenched, these ideas took on a tangible meaning. In the introduction of his paper Langmuir, stated the chemists' case as follows:

> "The problem of the structure of atoms has been attacked mainly by physicists who have given little consideration to the chemical properties which must ultimately be explained by a theory of atomic structure. The vast store of knowledge of chemical properties and relationships, such as is summarized by the Periodic Table, should serve as a better foundation for a theory of atomic structure than the relatively meager experimental data along purely physical lines."

Langmuir built on the electron pair and octet ideas of Lewis, which worked well for main group elements, and worked towards an explanation of the electron configuration of the transition metals, which he expressed in seven postulates.

---

[15] I. Langmuir. The arrangement of electrons in atoms and molecules. *J. Am. Chem. Soc.*, 1919, 41 (6), pp 868–934.

One of the points that the chemists seemed to have resolved (unlike the physics) was that the first electron shell could only have two electrons. Langmuir used arguments concerning symmetry and surface area to correctly argue that the shells of an atom must have capacities of 2, 8, 18 and 32 electrons. However, his order of filling was shell-by-shell (inside to outside), which runs into trouble when filling the transition metal and lanthanide shells ($n \geq 3$). Interestingly, he considered the electrons to have magnetic as well as electrostatic properties:

> *"Postulate 5.-It is assumed that electrons contained in the same cell are nearly without effect on each other. But the electrons in the outside layer tend to line themselves up (in a radial direction) with those of the underlying shell becaus of a magnetic field probably always to be associated with electrons bound in atoms. (Parson's magneton theory.) Thi attraction may be more or less counteracted by the electrostatic repulsion between the outside electrons and those in the underlying shell. The electrons in the outside layer also repel each other and thus tend to distribute themselves among the available cells so as to be as far apart as possible. The actual positions of equilibrium depend on a balance between these 3 sets of forces together with the attractive force exerted by the nucleus."*

After describing the atoms, Langmuir introduced more postulates and attempted to describe the bonding in molecules using a series of cubes where the corners represented electrons or places that electrons could be shared. This approach is reasonably successful in describing empirical formula, but fails at describing molecular shape.

It is interesting to see how Langmuir viewed the Bohr theory:

> "The recent advances in the physics of the electron have been largely along the lines of Bohr's theory. It is generally assumed that the electrons are revolving all in one plane, in orbits about the nucleus. Such a view is wholly inconsistent with that of the present paper. Bohr's theory has had marked success in explaining and even in predicting new facts connected with the spectra of hydrogen, helium and lithium, and must therefore contain important elements of truth. As has already been pointed out, Bohr's stationary states have a close resemblance to the cells postulated in the present theory. ... It will probably be possible to reconcile the two theories. ... In some such way we may hope to be led to a modification of Bohr's theory in which the electrons do not rotate about the nucleus."

The last statement, may be prophetic.

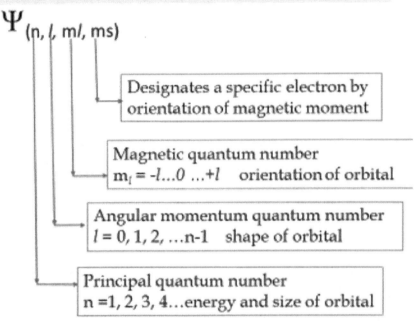

The Wave Function is a function of three quantum numbers that define the orbital and one quantum number that designates the electron

$\Psi_{(n, l, ml, ms)}$

Designates a specific electron by orientation of magnetic moment

Magnetic quantum number
$m_l = -l...0...+l$ orientation of orbital

Angular momentum quantum number
$l = 0, 1, 2, ...n-1$ shape of orbital

Principal quantum number
$n = 1, 2, 3, 4...$energy and size of orbital

When l = 0 the orbital is spherical (s-type)

When l = 1 the orbital is "dumb bell"-shaped (p-type) etc.

3.2 Atomic Orbitals

The Schrodinger model did not particularly mollify the chemists, but at least Schrodinger gave them a model of atoms that was 'visible' and three-dimensional. While the wave functions themselves with still mathematical abstractions, as shown above, the square-of-the-wave-function (Ψ^2) could be equated with electron density (locational probability) and by drawing a surface that contained some arbitrary (large) amount of the electron density (e.g., 90%), an atomic orbital could be visualized.

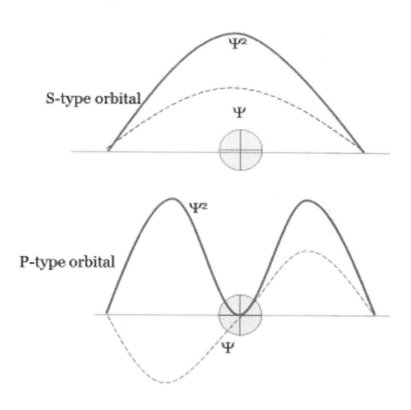

But the atomic orbitals did not conform to the bond angles and molecular symmetry *observed* by chemists.

3.3 Sigma and Pi Bonds

In 1927-28, Robert S. Mulliken (1896–1986) and Friedrich Hund (1896–1997) were extending the same ideas into the molecular orbital (MO) theory in which atomic orbitals were combined to make molecular orbitals (i.e., bonds between atoms). This idea came into full fruition in 1929 with John Edward Lennard-Jones (1894–1954) and his method of linear combinations of atomic orbitals (LCAO).

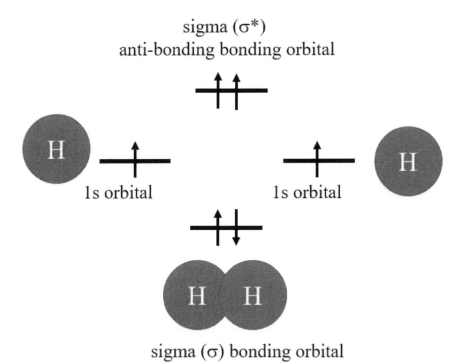

It gradually became apparent that the hybridization around atoms, which had (non-bonding) lone-pairs of electrons was

not perfectly as expected. In 1957, this led to the
introduction of the concept of valence shell electron-pair
repulsion theory (VSEPR).

After earning his doctorate, Erich Hückel (1896–1980)
worked with Peter Debye (1884–1966) in the 1920s to find a
way to account for electrostatic effects in electrolyte
solutions. He then spent part of 1928-29 with Niels Bohr
and undoubtedly followed the developing ideas of Pauling
about hybridization.   Hückel realized that after overlap of
atomic s and p orbitals to make bonding orbitals there were
"left-over" p-orbitals and that the close proximity of the
atoms allowed "left over" p-orbitals on adjacent atoms to
overlap concurrently with the direct (internuclear) overlap
of orbitals. He thus deduced that the direct overlap of the
2s and 2p) orbitals of carbon (as well as boron, oxygen,
nitrogen, etc.) created a (sigma) bond (symmetrical around
the interatomic axis), which allowed free rotation; but the
overlap of the 2p orbitals is not symmetrical around the
bond axis; indeed, it required a specific alignment, which
cannot be altered without breaking the (pi) bond. The
sigma/pi concept was expressed in 1930; and by 1931,
Hückel had developed valance bond (VB) and molecular
orbital (MO) descriptions of benzene. Unfortunately, he
was not very good at communicating his ideas and most of

the practical applications were developed decades later by others, especially Linus Pauling.

3.4 Linus Pauling and Hybrid Orbitals

When Linus Carl Pauling (1901–1994) received a PhD in physical chemistry in 1925 from the California Institute of Technology, the interpretation of atoms and electrons by Schrodinger and Pauli were on the table, but their description did not satisfy the needs of chemists. In 1932, Pauling realized that the s-type orbital and the set of three p-type orbitals were spherically symmetrical, but if he blended them together to obtain four sp^3 hybrid orbitals, he could rationalize tetrahedral symmetry around carbon (and other elements Li, Be, B, C, N, O, F, Ne). Suddenly everything fell into place.

The atomic orbitals were just mathematical representations and could be combined (by addition or subtraction) into linear combinations that were hybrids which could have any symmetry needed to accommodate binding in molecules. Nature was not constrained by atomic orbitals when seeking the lowest energy sate.

The covalent bonds between atoms involved overlap of orbitals from different atoms. Sometimes these were hybridized to place the electron density directly between the nuclei (sigma bonds). The sigma bond angles of 109.5°, 120° and 180° could be explained by hybridization of the s orbital with three p-orbitals (sp³), two p-orbitals (sp²) or one p-orbital (sp), respectively. Pauling refined his ideas in the 1930s and published his widely cited book *The Nature of the Chemical Bond* (first edition, 1939).

The process of hybridization can be illustrated qualitatively for simple systems. In the graphic below, I show the linear combinations of an s-type orbital with a p-type orbital. The two function are simply added and subtracted (Ψs+p and Ψs-p) to obtain linearly independent hybrids. The normalization constant is applied to ensure that the sum of the two hybrids squared is the same as the sum of the squares of the original atomic orbits.

$$(\Psi s)^2 + (\Psi p)^2 = (\Psi s+p)^2 + (\Psi s-p)^2$$

We have not changed the probabilities of finding the electron density, we have merely restructured it to conform to the realities of bonding in which the electron pairs repel one another while being attracted by the nuclei.

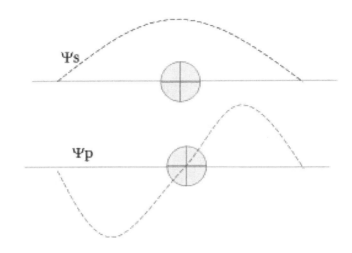

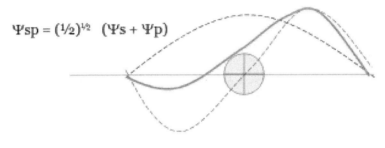

$\Psi sp = (\tfrac{1}{2})^{\tfrac{1}{2}} \; (\Psi s + \Psi p)$

$\Psi sp = (\tfrac{1}{2})^{\tfrac{1}{2}} \; (\Psi s - \Psi p)$

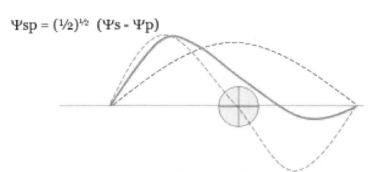

Two-dimensional plots of sp-hybrid orbitals

The overlap of Pauling's *hybridized* atomic orbitals following the molecular orbital concepts of Hückel could, thus, fully explain structural (organic and inorganic) chemistry.

For more details I encourage you to read my books "*History of Atomic Theory*" and "*Organic Chemistry and informal history.*"

Printed in Great Britain
by Amazon

78889669R00032

joy in God

REKINDLING
AN INNER FIRE

Joachim Hartmann and
Annette Clara Unkelhäußer

Designed by Messenger Publications Design Department
Typeset in Town 80 & Liorah BT
Printed by Hussar Books

Messenger Publications,
37 Leeson Place, Dublin D02 E5V0
www.messenger.ie

Contents

Preface

There is a well-known saying: 'Speech is silver and silence is golden.' Familiar and believable, it rings true but it is only one side of the coin. The other side is 'Speech is golden'. That is the theme we consider in this book.

In the story of the healing of the dumb demoniac in Matthew's Gospel (Matthew 9:32f.) the exorcism of the demon causing muteness demonstrates just what a precious gift speech is, the ability to communicate one's self to others. The philosopher Plato chooses dialogue to address the essential questions about humankind and life. For St Ignatius of Loyola, the essence of a living relationship is the 'mutual communication between the two persons' (Spiritual Exercises – SE – 231). Jesus himself is called the 'Word made flesh'. It was through his words that Jesus, a master of words, enabled people to have healing encounters. 'What's wrong?' 'What do you want?' 'What are you looking for?' 'Why are you weeping?' Hearing these questions, people must have felt: 'Here is someone who cares, who has time for me and who wants to listen to me.'

The Road to Emmaus (Luke 24:13–35) is a vivid example of speech being golden. The disciples are distraught and subdued because their Master has been crucified. Jesus joins them on the road and asks: 'What are you discussing with each other while you walk along?' (Luke 24:17). By communicating their thoughts and feelings to Jesus, they gradually gain a deeper insight into the events of the previous days. Their eyes are opened in different ways. The fire of their faith is rekindled. That Gospel story is the continuous thread running through the conversations in this book.

During the courses held at our retreat house, we experience what a valuable contribution the various forms of communication make to the process of the retreat. The silence that is practised and the conversations that take place between each individual retreatant and their guide complement each other in a fruitful way. It is in the silence that we learn to be present, listening and being aware of what *is*. This awareness in silence forms the basis for communication. Through the silence, key issues can surface. Articulating and communicating these becomes the starting point for conversation between the individual retreatant and guide.

Haus Gries retreat house in Bavaria, Germany, was founded by Father Franz Jalics SJ in 1984. He developed the 'Gries Path' of contemplation. In his best-selling book, *Contemplative Retreat – An Introduction to a Contemplative Way of Life and the Jesus Prayer*, he describes this path, which we continue to teach in our ten-day courses.

Its basis is twofold: i) continuous silence and ii) communal prayer times held in the silence of the group. In addition, each day there is an opportunity for individual retreatants to meet with their guides for one-to-one spiritual accompaniment and for communicating whatever is emerging from their inner journey. The day ends with a communal celebration of the Eucharist. This includes reflections, based on Holy Scripture, on central themes of the spiritual journey.

The Gries Path leading to the Jesus Prayer is composed of a series of exercises or steps. We begin with awareness exercises out in nature and then move on to body-awareness exercises. Here, we accompany our breath on its journey through the body. The next exercise is awareness of our hands, seeing the middle of our palms as a door that can lead us into the present moment. Our practice of contemplative prayer continues, focusing on a word. We listen to the way it resounds within us or the way in which it invites us to move into a relationship with it. This way of prayer is comparable to that found in the Spiritual Exercises of Ignatius (SE 238). The succession of words used, one building upon the other, is: Yes, Mary and Jesus Christ. The Jesus Prayer forms the heart of the Gries Path. The Jesus Prayer can be found in other spiritual traditions, but in the way it is used on the Gries Path it has its own profile.

In this book we speak of 'contemplation', 'contemplative prayer' and 'contemplative retreats' rather than 'meditation', because the word *contemplari* (to look, to gaze) aptly expresses the goal of our spiritual journey: 'We will see him as he is' (1 John 3:2). Similarly, the word contemplation names awareness as the way to this goal.

The words contemplation and meditation can take on different meanings depending on the school of thought. Nowadays meditation is the term for many different practices of self-awareness. They all aim at bringing people closer to themselves. We understand meditation in the classic Ignatian use of the word: a way of consciously dealing with thoughts, feelings, images and texts. Thinking about and reflecting on these is then at the forefront of our awareness.

Contemplation, as we understand it and are using it here, is an alert attentiveness which does not take other sources such as texts or 'material' as its focus, but is characterised by simplicity and silence. What is foremost here is quite simply being present, being aware, staying alert, letting things happen and receiving.

On the Gries Path contemplation is described as *Christian* because our attention is directed to the Name, and therefore to the presence of Jesus Christ. Furthermore, this way of contemplation is interpreted from within the Christian tradition: from Scripture, from the Desert Fathers and from the mystics.

In contemplation it is not a matter of thinking about something, it is about being completely and immediately attentive to the present moment, allowing whatever happens in the silence, when oriented on the presence of God, to reveal itself.

The idea for this book originated from the desire to make more widely available the valued experiences that emerge through the conversations between retreatants and guides. We want to present the key topics and make them accessible to others.

The individual chapters of the book, each based on a particular theme, have a clear and consistent structure. A short introduction to the theme is followed by a conversation. Scripture, the writings of St Ignatius, experiences from spiritual accompaniment and our own personal experience form the basis for these conversations. Using the questions, 'Where was my heart burning?' 'Where were my eyes opened?' we pick out the aspects of the conversation that triggered a particular resonance within ourselves. Finally, each chapter concludes with short exercises for the reader, relevant to the theme.

We have found the form of a spiritual conversation to be the most inspiring and illuminative for the purposes of this book. Like the disciples on the road to Emmaus we experienced, time and again, that 'our eyes were opened' or that 'our hearts were burning'. Gazing at Jesus Christ the *silver* of speech was converted into *gold*.

1
AWARENESS AND TRUST

Introduction

Occasionally when out on a walk we come across signs pointing to a 'Senses trail'. As we follow it, we are invited to become particularly aware of our senses. Some people, exploring their senses, are more adventurous: for example, dining wearing a blindfold, allowing themselves to be waited on and led. Others make astonishing discoveries when they simply allow themselves to taste different foods. There is a great need for the rediscovery of our senses. These are the doors that open for us the entrance into the world of awareness.

Awakening our ability to be aware and encouraging us to use it was of utmost importance for Jesus. Awareness is part of who we are, but it is frequently neglected. As a result, we can be unaware of God as the 'I am who I am' (Exodus 3: 14) or as the 'I am here'. In the gospels, Jesus heals those who are blind and deaf. We can take that as a sign that our human perceptive faculty is often defective and in need of restoration.

Franz Jalics's Contemplative Way is a school for perception, for awareness. We learn to become aware once again and, in doing so, to trust that awareness will lead us into the presence of God.

Conversation

Joachim:
The Gries Path is a school of contemplation. What, for you, is its main characteristic?

Annette Clara:
Its clear technique. Out of many years of experience, Franz Jalics developed a way of bringing people, step by step, to the Name of Jesus Christ. These steps are given in his book *Contemplative Retreat*.

J: These steps are in a very specific order. We begin with focusing on nature, then on our breathing. Then we turn our attention to the palms of our hands and then to a word within us. Finally, we move into praying the Name of Jesus Christ. Although we don't begin with it, the name, Jesus Christ, is central to the Gries Path.

AC: That's right. First of all, we have to learn to stay attentively with something because being aware presupposes being able to be attentive. The steps guiding us prepare us for being aware of the presence of God. This is why we practise being attentive in the present moment and remaining there. Thomas Aquinas said that there is no prayer without being attentive. French philosopher and mystic Simone Weil writes: 'Absolutely unmixed attention is prayer'.

J: This kind of awareness or these attention exercises are also part of Mindfulness-based Stress Reduction (MBSR), a programme developed by Jon Kabat-Zinn in the late 1970s in the USA. It aims at reducing stress by using a guided focusing of attention. His approach is still prevalent. Jon Kabat-Zinn was invited to give awareness meditations to participants from the economic elite at the World Economic Forum at Davos in 2015. But what is the difference between this and the Gries Path?

AC: I think there are a number of similarities. I appreciate Jon Kabat-Zinn's approach. However, the 'Gries Path' should not be seen in a medical context, but rather in a religious one. I think because of this it has a different emphasis. We are not practising awareness in order to attain any particular effects, such as reducing stress or getting healed. We are practising without any intention or purpose. We just want to be there for God. Contemplation means gazing or being aware. We might ask why do we have to practise being aware at all?

J: We have forgotten what we could do naturally when we were children: lingering and dwelling on something with absolute attentiveness and so in pure wonder, discovering the world about us. We live in a world where so much is going on and where, particularly in the media, the aim is to distract us. Awareness exercises are ways to help us to focus ourselves. By doing so, our attentiveness gains strength, much like sunbeams when they are converged through a magnifying glass. This leads us to pure awareness.

AC: There's something else as well. When we are practising contemplative prayer, we allow our minds to rest, without their becoming active. However, we can be very composed when we are thinking about certain things or we can be very concentrated when doing particular activities. Why is it so important for the Gries Path of Contemplation *not* to start thinking or doing anything?

11

J: Good question. Normally we approach life in three stages: perceiving, thinking and doing. In our performance-oriented world, thinking and doing take up too much space. Perception is often considerably under-utilised. Hardly have we perceived something, than we begin to analyse and evaluate it and immediately move towards action. That is why for contemplative prayer we practise perceiving only. If our thinking and doing are a result of our perception then we can continue to be prayerful in these areas as well.

AC: Was Jesus contemplative?

J: Yes, absolutely. His way of thinking and doing came wholly from his awareness and his trust. We can only be aware in the present moment. Even if our perception is of something from the past, the perception itself takes place in the present moment. That means that Jesus was constantly present. When he says: 'So do not worry about tomorrow, tomorrow will take care of itself' (Matthew 6:34), he is inviting us to live totally in the present moment. Perception also has a lot to do with trust. If we are completely in the present, we can feel that God cares for us. This may open up a new and more relaxed view of my perception of my past or my consideration of the future.

AC: Exactly! These two basic attitudes of awareness and trust are what we develop in contemplative prayer. We perceive what *is*, let it be there, working on us, without changing anything, and entrust ourselves completely to God's guidance. Franz Jalics formulates it like this: 'We change from the driving seat of our life to the passenger seat and let God take over the steering wheel of our life.' And that has a lot to do with trust. I know that from my own experience of being a passenger. I find it difficult not to take over and to trust that everything will be fine.

J: Isn't there a danger of being passive in life if we hand over responsibility?

AC: We have to discern carefully. When we train our awareness in silence, then we are orienting ourselves on the presence of God. However, at the same time we are aware of what is arising from within us. Perception, as we understand it, reveals what moves us and what wants to be seen. And it is exactly this that allows us to discern how to act in the situations of our life.

J: Why do we take the path of awareness and trusting in God's guidance and not just do as we think best?

AC: I'll try to make it clearer: It is only our awareness and our orientation on God that make it possible for us to realise what we *really* want. They are the basis for clear, self-determined and important decisions.

J: In spiritual accompaniment, sometimes it is necessary to check that people are going in the right direction. This is the question: How do I know that I can trust my perception?

AC: In relation to perception, it is so important for both retreatant and guide to look and consider it together. This is why their conversations are an integral part of the contemplative retreats in Haus Gries.

J: Trust, then, also means talking to the guide and confiding in him or her.

AC: Exactly. A special feature of Haus Gries with regard to the individual or one-to-one conversations is that they are not of a specific length. Because of this, it is possible each time to give as much time as somebody needs. Jesus had a great insight for both the correct timing and for the right time, the *kairos*. Let's take a look at Scripture. Where are contemplative attitudes most clearly expressed for you?

J: There is a wonderful statement in the story of Hagar in Genesis 16:13: 'I have seen the one who sees me.' Another striking passage is in the First Letter of John, where a goal for the journey of a Christian is given: 'We shall see him as he really is.'

AC: And there is also that splendid text in Matthew's Gospel: 'Look at the birds in the sky. They do not sow or reap or gather into barns, yet your heavenly Father feeds them' (Matthew 6:26). And later in the text: 'Set your hearts on his kingdom first, and on his righteousness, and all these other things will be given you as well' (Matthew 6:33).

J: Your examples from Matthew 6 show that awareness and trust are attitudes that we need in daily life and ones that Jesus encourages us to have: Look at how it is going and recognise the laws of life. Basically, the whole Bible expresses a contemplative view of life. This is why it makes sense to read the Bible contemplatively. The Second Vatican Council emphasised that the Bible should be read in the spirit in which it was written. And it was written gazing at Jesus Christ.

AC: Also, Ignatius invites us to be aware and to trust. '*Sentir*' – to feel – is a key word for Ignatius. In his Spiritual Exercises he invites his retreatants to use what is called the Application of the Senses by using their five senses to perceive a biblical passage more deeply (SE 121–125). It is also worth noting here his famous comment: 'What fills and satisfies the soul consists, not in knowing much, but in our understanding the realities profoundly and in savouring them interiorly' (SE 2). His plea for trust is: 'Few people realise what God would do for them if they were to place themselves wholly into his hands.'

J: I have experienced the power of perception myself. When I made my first contemplative retreat, it went very deep. Consistently, refraining from thinking and searching for knowledge made the deep drilling into my soul possible and sustained me from within.

AC: My former colleagues have also noticed how effective contemplative prayer is. When I went on contemplative retreats they used to ask, 'Why don't you do something proper? There are so many worthwhile projects around that you could usefully do as a Christian.' Over the years, however, they changed their opinion. When I was stressed at work or couldn't listen as well as usual, they would ask, 'Why don't you go on a contemplative retreat again?'!

J: Your example shows that awareness and trust lead us to the very centre of life. The contemplative way helps us to be in the present moment and to recognise better what needs to be done at any given moment. As such, it takes us right into the middle of the world. Living their contemplative lives to the full, people like Madeleine Delbrel or Dag Hammarskjöld were both socially and politically active. Madeleine Delbrel was involved in social justice in twentieth-century France. Dag Hammarskjöld, a UN politician and General Secretary of the United Nations, received the Nobel Peace Prize.

AC: It is important for the renewal of our society that people in responsible positions in the business, political and social fields are encouraged to get to know the way of awareness and trust.

15

Making the ten-day retreat in Haus Gries can be a bit difficult, though. A manager once told me that the Gries Path was a great idea but asked how he could fit it into his busy daily life. What would you say to him?

J: Contemplation is already in our everyday life and can be discovered there. I would advise him to think about what gives him strength in his daily life, where there are spaces that haven't been earmarked for anything else, spaces where he can relax. I would encourage him to go on a journey of discovery with openness and interest and to invest in these ten days of experiencing himself and God on a contemplative retreat.

AC: And I would suggest three different ways in which he can practise contemplation in his daily life: In the evening he could do the 'daily examen', a prayer of loving awareness at the end of the day, asking himself, 'What has been successful today? What am I grateful for? What moved me especially? What was difficult?' This kind of review trains us in awareness and our perception blossoms. When he is on his way to work or out on a walk he can consciously practise concentrating on only one sense so that he is 'all ears' or 'all eyes'. A third way would be for him to squeeze in a 'breathing space' at work in which he consciously looks within himself and asks: 'How am I fully present right now?'

J: We have been journeying quite a way with each other. It's time for us to take a moment to pause and to reflect on the effect that the conversation has had on us. Like the disciples on the road to Emmaus we want to ask ourselves:

Where were my eyes opened?
Where was my heart burning?

J: My eyes were opened at the insight that before I can think or act, I need to have been fully aware of the situation. A problem with perception, therefore, means a problem with the subsequent thought process or action. This shows just how necessary schools of awareness are for personal well-being and common good.

AC: My heart was burning at the insight that awareness is the 'yeast' that can change the world.

Exercises:
15 minutes silence

I ask myself: Whilst I was reading, where were my eyes opened and where was my heart burning?

I go for a short walk in the garden or out in nature and practise being aware with every one of my senses.

I notice: Where were my eyes opened?
Where was my heart burning?

2
GRATITUDE
AND JOY

Introduction

Who doesn't know the positive effects of a smile, or of the lights flashing 'Thank you!' when we leave a village having kept to the speed limit, or even a friendly acknowledgement when we greet someone with a 'Good morning!' Gratitude and joy are infectious, a compass directing us towards life. Yet true joy and gratitude are not so easy to find. It is a waste of neither time nor money when firms invest in 'laughter seminars' for their employees.

Books about positive thinking are plentiful. The fine arts also express joy and gratitude in so many different ways. For example, in Friedrich Schiller's poem 'Ode to Joy' we read: 'Joy commands the hardy mainspring / Of the universe eterne. / Joy, oh joy the wheel is driving / Which the worlds' great clock doth turn. / Flowers from the buds she coaxes, / Suns from out the hyaline, / Spheres she rotates through expanses, / Which the seer can't divine.' (trans. W. Wertz)

Scripture provides many pointers towards gratitude and joy: 'The joy of the Lord is your strength' (Nehemiah 8:10) is a strong expression of it. Despite this, Christians are often criticised for being stern and miserable. As such, they are hardly going to convince other people about their way of life, let alone inspire them.

Conversation

Joachim:
The topic of gratitude and joy is particularly close to your heart, Annette Clara, isn't it? Why is that?

Annette Clara:
The word 'gospel' means 'good news'. But do we ever feel the joy or the exuberance of the Christian message? In homilies scriptural texts are not often interpreted from this perspective. That's why it is important for me to bring the precious jewel of joy in the Scriptures back into people's awareness. Another reason is the interaction between joy and gratitude. Joy is the key to gratitude and gratitude increases joy.

J: It's worth noting that Jesus puts gratitude into the very centre of the Last Supper. He gives thanks for his life and his mission, and in spite of the dreadfulness of the situation we are told: 'Jesus took bread and when he had said the blessing he broke it' (Matthew 26:26). It is as if he wanted to doubly underline the importance of gratitude and to make us take it deeply to heart. It is obvious that his gratitude does not have its roots in the concrete situation of his forthcoming Passion, but from a much deeper level. We celebrate the Eucharist in memory of the Last Supper. We are glad that our resurrected Lord is truly present and we are filled with gratitude for what we receive from him. The Greek word 'eucharist' means thanksgiving.

AC: The apostle Paul took Jesus' example completely to heart. He pleads insistently for an attitude of gratitude and joy when he says: 'Always be joyful; pray constantly; in every situation give thanks' (1 Thessalonians 5:16–18). We should remember that Paul had a hard life. He was persecuted and thrown into prison, but he lived from a profound faith which gave him strength and support and bore much fruit. He understands being a pastoral minister as not lording it over people's faith but rather being partners of their joy (cf. 2 Corinthians 1:24).

J: A further dimension needs to be looked at when we think about this triad of being joyful, thankful and praying: that we should be joyful 'at all times', pray 'constantly' and be thankful 'for everything'. Isn't that rather overwhelming? How do you understand Paul's teaching, which does not give a time limit and which seems to refer to everything?

AC: I think it's a matter of being present to the present moment. St Paul talks about the dimension of what remains constant in the midst of life's changes. It is as if he wants to say: If you can keep this state that comes from the connection you have with the ever-present God, then you have everything that you need. Awareness of being in the presence of God fills St Paul with gratitude and also with hope for the future: 'We know that for those who love God, everything works together for good' (Romans 8:28).

J: Can we do anything to foster this state of being present to the present moment?

AC: Yes. St Ignatius suggests taking time every day to do the prayer of loving awareness (also known as the daily examen or review), choosing three things from each day for which you are particularly thankful. It works! Neurological research confirms this. If we focus on what is positive, we change the connections in our brain. An upward trend is set in motion and positive feelings like joy, happiness and satisfaction increase. Regular prayer or meditation has a verifiable effect on our brain, as has been shown by tests on Tibetan monks who have been through years of spiritual meditative practice. Nevertheless, there are also people who are always grateful for everything, yet who leave me feeling unsettled. How does that come about?

J: One reason could be that for these people their being grateful fends off difficult situations and emotions so that conflict can be avoided.

AC: This is true for our daily review as well. I once had a person in spiritual accompaniment who allowed only positive issues to crop up in their daily examen. Over time, this person became more and more aggressive. It was only when failure was also given space to be acknowledged in the daily review that inner peace was able to flow.

J: That is a good example of the difference between the technique of positive thinking and the Ignatian prayer of loving awareness. Because we trust in God, who wants everything to work for good, we can allow everything to come into our awareness in the daily review, not just what is positive. We do not try to steer things in a positive direction. We can allow rebellion within ourselves and say a 'no' that need not be skipped. I can put this negative into God's hands as well.

AC: Ignatian retreats are a school of joy and gratitude. In the 'fourth week' St Ignatius gives us the instruction 'to ask for the grace to be glad and to rejoice intensely because of the great glory and joy of Christ our Lord' (SE 221). Likewise, Ignatius invites us to cast a grateful look over our whole life: 'to ask for interior knowledge of all the great good I have received ... [to be] stirred to profound gratitude' (SE 233). Giving thanks for all the good things that have happened in my life is often a way into a more inclusive gratitude. The Jesuit priest Alfred Delp made a moving plea for gratitude when he wrote in his letters from a cell in the Berlin-Tegel prison on 17 November 1944: 'One thing is as clear and as tangible as seldom before: The world is so full of God. From every gap or crack of everything he wells up, as it were, towards us. We, however, are often blind. We stay trapped in the beautiful and the evil hours and do not experience them tracing back to the depths of the wellspring from which they flow out of God. This is true for everything that is beautiful as well as evil: in everything God wants to celebrate encounter and asks for and wants a worshipping, surrendering answer … '.

J: Alfred Delp shows himself here to be a thoroughly aware person. It is exactly this that we foster in contemplative retreats: being completely present and receptive to what wells up from the fullness of presence. Our response to this is joy and gratitude.

AC: On the 'Gries Path' of contemplation the awareness exercises of the first day spent in nature are well-established. Our five senses are the simplest way into awareness that we have: seeing, hearing, smelling, feeling and tasting. For example, we practise being 'all ears' or 'all eyes' by letting a tree work on us, or by listening to the twittering of the birds. We stay with the simple perception of whatever draws our attention without reflecting on it or evaluating it.

J: You have spoken about nature. By doing this exercise, many retreatants discover just how much beauty there is around them. They are often unable to be aware of it because they are lost in their thoughts or in their worries. Gratitude and joy are awakened by their being aware of their surroundings. Gratitude and joy are so basic that I am surprised that the gospels never directly mention that Jesus was happy. We hear that he wept or that he was angry. I would find it comforting to find a passage where Jesus was happy or laughed.

AC: The issue of Jesus and laughter arises in the novel *The Name of the Rose*. The Franciscan friar William of Baskerville has a discussion with Jorge, a monk who preaches about Jesus' being serious. Baskerville asks, 'I wonder why you are so hostile to the idea that Jesus could have laughed.'

J: Perhaps joy was so much a part of Jesus and his life that the evangelists did not specifically mention it. The only mention of Jesus' joy is in St John's Gospel: 'I have told you this so that my own joy may be in you, and your joy may be complete' (John 15:11). Perhaps Jesus was himself the personification of joy. Perhaps 'perfect joy' means this 'being-fully-joyful'?

AC: The meeting between the two pregnant women, Elizabeth and Mary, affirms this. Elizabeth says to Mary, 'As soon as your greeting reached my ears, the child in my womb leapt for joy' (Luke 1:44). In Elizabeth's womb John feels the presence of Jesus in Mary and is glad. When Mary hears of this joy, there awakens in her great joy which she expresses in the Magnificat: 'My soul proclaims the greatness of the Lord and my spirit rejoices in God my Saviour' (Luke 1:46f).

J: Meeting people who live out of joy and gratitude is infectious and awakens gratitude and joy in others.

AC: That's very true. I remember an elderly woman who came for counselling with her daughter who was so seriously ill that she could no longer work. Ideally, more sessions were necessary but the daughter was unable to continue. However, in spite of many difficulties it was finally possible to organise a disability allowance for her. The elderly mother was over the moon. After that she visited me in my office every year shortly before Christmas, coming into town by bus, bringing me home-made biscuits, a plant and a card. She thanked me again and again for my help as if it had been only the day before. This touched me deeply and joy and gratitude intensified in me as well. Through her behaviour she showed me that I too can be thankful for the successes in my work.

J: It is important for every enterprise to foster a culture of gratitude. It is not for nothing that there are many ways in which employers show their employees that their work is appreciated. This contributes to creating a good atmosphere at work. Ingratitude, on the other hand, never bears much fruit. In a letter from 18 March 1542 Ignatius writes that ingratitude is the fundamental evil of humanity.

AC: That makes sense. Ingratitude has a very negative impact – envy and jealousy, greed and arrogance. When I thank someone, I am acknowledging that I am receiving something that is good for me. It also shows me that I need something from others and that I cannot give myself everything. On the other hand, if I am arrogant, I think that I owe everything to myself. Grateful people are less likely to be envious or jealous because they appreciate and acknowledge that they themselves are recipients.

J: We have been walking quite a way with each other now. It's time for us to take a moment to pause and to reflect on the effect that the conversation has had on us. Like the disciples on the road to Emmaus we want to ask ourselves:

Where were my eyes opened?
Where was my heart burning?

AC: My eyes were opened when I realised that simply *being* brings joy because even in deep pain I can still feel that I am not alone. It is enough just to be in the presence of God.

J: My heart was burning when I realised that I could understand Jesus who, as the personification of joy, awakened joy in people simply through his presence.

Exercises: 15 minutes silence

I take time to reflect: Where were my eyes opened when I was reading? Where was my heart burning?

I call to mind three things or situations during my life for which I am particularly grateful.

When was the moment of greatest joy in my life?

3
I
AND
YOU

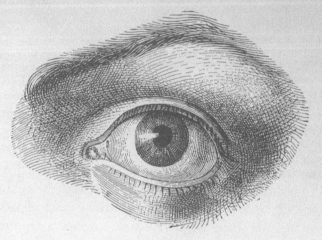

Introduction

People are relational beings, created to seek another, a 'you'. Nevertheless we are often confronted with our own egoism or with the egoism of others. We long to be seen, we long for real encounter, yet we often suffer from a lack of personal relationships and from isolation. We desire a life with depth, yet we run away from ourselves, diverting ourselves with any number of distractions. Is there some kind of medicine to heal us from the sicknesses of a false self-centredness and lead us into living relationships?

Conversation

Joachim:
In his Spiritual Exercises, Ignatius described the best medicine for spiritual growth in this way: 'For everyone ought to reflect that in all spiritual matters, the more one divests oneself of self-love, self-will and self-interest, the more progress one will make.' (SE 189). How does that sound?

Annette Clara:
I think we still have to discern more. Having a mind of my own is invaluable for my spiritual life and also has something to do with decisiveness and orientation. A saying that I learned in my childhood is probably more apt for me: " 'I want' is a powerful phrase, but if it is spoken seriously and quietly, then the little phrase 'I want' pulls the stars off the sky.' "

J: Ignatius has great respect for willpower and certainly had a mind of his own. He would definitely have liked the quotation from your childhood. He said, 'Whoever really wants something, will find that nothing is difficult.' In his opinion it is a matter of how and to what our will is oriented that is important. Are we only circling around ourselves or are we also looking at others?

AC: Another way of putting it would be to ask: Am I making myself the centre of my life or can I perceive that I am part of a greater whole? Following Copernicus's way of thinking: Can I perceive that I am like the earth, which moves round the sun? Or am I living as if the sun and everything was moving around me? In our spiritual lives we have to repeat the Copernican revolution again and again.

J: From a Christian perspective, the Copernican revolution is nothing other than being centred on someone else, that is to say, being 'focused on you'.

AC: This runs through the Bible like a continuous thread. God constantly appeals to us to put HIM in first place and to make HIM the centre of our lives.

J: Two passages are important for me in this context: In the narrative about Creation we hear how humankind stopped being 'focused on you' because they wanted to be the centre themselves. As a result, they lost their orientation on God and contact with themselves. God asks: 'Where are you, Adam?' (Genesis 3:9). This question describes the state of the person who is not living in the present moment, which is where life takes place. Another striking passage is in the first chapter of John's Gospel. When the first disciples want to follow Jesus, he turns to them and asks them: 'What are you looking for?' (John 1:38). Here Jesus is completely 'focused on you'. His question puts the disciples in touch with themselves. They should notice what is moving them, where they come from and what they are longing for.

AC: That reminds me of John the Baptist. He recognises in Jesus someone who is greater than himself and he does not bind his followers to himself but frees them by pointing elsewhere: 'Look, there is the Lamb of God' (John 1:29). This is a shining example of being 'focused on you'.

J: The Isenheim altarpiece has a very impressive artistic portrayal of this scene. John the Baptist is depicted with an oversized index finger pointing out Jesus.

AC: John the Baptist's approach is trailblazing for spiritual accompaniment. To my mind, he is the patron of spiritual accompaniment. If we are ambitious and want to achieve specific results, then we stand in God's way. Instead of doing that, we ought to let HIS guidance flow through us. As spiritual companions we are the ground staff who are allowed to assist in God's salvation of humankind.

J: Can you give me an example from spiritual accompaniment?

AC: A woman who was in great distress came for a conversation. I wanted to help her and made every effort to understand her so that I could offer her some kind of advice or solution. But her thoughts and questions were so confusing that I came under increasing pressure. Finally I reached the point when I felt within myself: 'I need to give up the desire to understand and to give advice and "just be there".' This was the decisive change from 'I' to 'you'. At the end of the conversation she said to me: 'Many thanks. You have been of great help to me. I now know the way forward.' She had carried both the problem and its solution within her and had simply needed someone who was there and prepared to listen.

J: That is a good example of a contemplative approach. Using our attention and all our interest we learn to be able to listen to people with an attitude of openness to what is happening and with no hidden agenda. We do not want to aim at any results. We simply remain there, aware. This is what we practise on the Gries Path of contemplation. We learn specific exercises that help us to focus our attention, to be alert and interested and to remain in the present moment.

AC: The contemplative path is a school of 'focusing on you'. We move from revolving around ourselves to focusing on God. Thinking in terms of the story of Creation, when we are on the contemplative path we are turning round and starting to move back in the direction of Paradise. We are not alone in doing so because Jesus wants to prepare the way for us and lead us back to God. He is the expert in 'focusing on you'. He asks people what is worrying them, what they want. He listens with all his heart and by doing so he touches the person in their inmost being so that they open themselves up and entrust themselves to him. Jesus is also in tune with what he himself needs. He withdraws time and again into solitude and prayers, totally focused on the Father.

J: This reminds me of what Jesus calls the greatest commandment (Mark 12:29–31), to love God, my neighbour and myself. There is a similar threefold invitation in the importance of being 'focused on you'. I can understand it with regard to being focused on God and my neighbour but what does 'focusing on you' mean with regard to myself?

AC: It means that I am aware of myself as an individual, that I am aware of what I need. If I exploit myself by treating myself as an object, then I am not aware of myself as 'you'. I am thinking here of what I have seen in the fitness centre over many years. People train there whatever the cost. I remember one woman in particular. She had a demanding job and was also looking after her elderly parents. After work and before her caring tasks she raced into the fitness centre. She was a petite and exhausted person who nevertheless worked out mercilessly with the heaviest weights. The slogan of the centre was: 'I am at the centre'.

J: Your example is revealing for me. Even good things like sport, caring for my body, can go in the wrong direction if I do not pay attention to my own needs, am unaware of the signals my body is sending and, instead, use my body like a performance machine.

AC: 'Focusing on you' with regard to myself is important not only in sport but in all other spheres of life. There are a lot of people who are barely in touch with themselves. This is also noticeable on retreat. On the whole, retreatants generally need about three days to 'arrive' and to reach a starting point for contemplative prayer. Many are amazed at just how tired and exhausted they are.

J: One reason for the lack of self-awareness nowadays is the tendency that people have to distract themselves rather than unwind or rest in themselves. Distraction is a defensive reflex: not wanting to see or feel or look at anything unpleasant within myself and my life. There is a negative culture of distraction: watching TV for hours on end, or directing a great deal of my attention to my smartphone; constant exposure to background noise and screens whilst shopping, at the doctor or on trains and planes. The contemplative path goes in the opposite direction. We learn how to be in touch with ourselves, to rest in ourselves, to feel ourselves.

AC: Feeling is a key word. A young man who had just finished the contemplative retreat at Haus Gries for the first time said on leaving: 'I have felt properly in contact with myself for the first time: I feel I am in the here and now and alive.' An important way into his life, his feelings and his faith had been opened for him through practising awareness.

J: We have spoken a lot about 'focusing on you' with regard to ourselves. This is the direct opposite of egocentricity. The Christian tradition speaks of three signs of egocentricity: addiction to possessions (greed), addiction to power and addiction to ambition. These can affect our prayer. Some examples are if my prayer is focused on results, if I want to have something, if I am proud of the way I pray, if I am seeking extraordinary experiences or if I want to have control of my spiritual journey and in many other ways too. What helps you, Annette Clara, to orient yourself towards God in your daily life?

AC: The way I begin and the way I end the day are my mainstays. In the morning I begin with a passage from the Bible that focuses me and accompanies me throughout the day. In the evening I turn to St Ignatius's examen, his prayer of loving awareness, with the following questions: Where was I present? What am I grateful for? What was not so successful? Can I place the day as it is into God's hands? Sometimes I find it helpful to put my hands together quite deliberately and to be aware of them, or else to make the Sign of the Cross. The Sign of the Cross is, of course, a very concentrated sign of 'focusing on you'. It is a deliberate sign of intention to be clearly focused on God. And, of course, praying contemplatively has a fixed place in my daily routine. Do you also have rituals that help you to orient yourself on God in your daily life?

J: Apart from having explicit fixed times for contemplative prayer, the way I begin and end the day is important for me too. If I am at work and have a lot to do, I sometimes find it helpful to pause for a minute, to sit down and breathe deeply, or I take a turn around the house in order to take an inward step back from myself. Then I find that I can be in touch with myself again and have a healthy approach to things. Sometimes the Jesus Prayer helps, or simply the Lord's Prayer. The Our Father is the only prayer that Jesus left us. It is a prayer and a testament to the importance of 'focusing on you': 'Our Father in heaven, hallowed be *your* Name, *your* kingdom come, *your* will be done' (Matthew 6:9f). If we put the God of love in first place, our desires and endeavours all fall into place.

AC: The question of 'I and you' does not concern humankind only as individuals but affects humanity as a whole. I am thinking about politics. If it is socially acceptable to follow only the interests of one's own country, then that is a form of egocentricity that has serious consequences for the entire global community. 'America first' is a recent example of this. There needs to be a 'focusing on you' in politics, too, an awareness of the global community and its interconnection. I am thinking of the resources of the earth, of climate protection, of hunger in the world and of the maintenance or restoration of peace. Democracy itself constantly demands a culture of dialogue, of confrontation and of the struggle to find a solution for the good of all.

J: World politics as it is today is a tug of war between the attitudes of egocentricity and 'focusing on you'. The threatening disintegration of Europe and the challenge to democracy are the frightening effects of a lack of 'focusing on you'.

AC: We have been walking quite a way with each other now. It's time for us to take a moment to pause and to reflect on the effect that the conversation has had on us. Like the disciples on the road to Emmaus we want to ask ourselves:

Where were my eyes opened?
Where was my heart burning?

J: My eyes were opened to see how precious it is to be able to make up my own mind and to be aware of where my will is focused.

AC: My heart was burning when I realised that the fate of the world and of peace essentially depends on practising 'focusing on you' on an individual *and* at a collective level.

Exercises:
15 minutes silence

Where was my heart burning when I was reading this?
Where were my eyes opened?

I look within myself to see if, at the moment, there are any examples in my life where I am over-attached, if not addicted, to possessions or power or ambition.

I ask myself: 'Where do I want to have or get as much as I possibly can?' 'Are there situations in which I try to dominate others or to take the first place?'

I look for a ritual that is suitable for my daily life which will help me to be more 'focused on you' in all its meanings.

4
EMPTINESS
AND FULNESS

Introduction

Jesus says to his disciples: 'It is easier for a camel to pass through the eye of a needle than for someone rich to enter the kingdom of God' (Mark 10:25). With this Jesus puts his finger on a central aspect of Christian life: our willingness to become empty or to become poor before God. The disciples are shocked because they sense how difficult it is to be really empty and poor. This is the passage that, time and again, leads to misunderstandings: should we all be poor, not own anything, be ascetic? Does Jesus begrudge us everything? It is HE who has promised us a life in fullness. The word 'emptiness' is not easily understood because it can be interpreted in so many different ways. For one thing it sounds negative. Yet it is exactly our willingness to become empty that is essential for our spiritual life. This is why it plays an integral role in contemplative retreats.

Conversation

Joachim:

The use of the word 'emptiness' in this topic gives the impression that it is pointing towards a deficiency and an unfulfilled life.

Annette Clara:

Yes, that's right. Emptiness can indeed be a deficiency, but there can also be a fullness in the emptiness. When this is the case the emptiness expresses a readiness to be open in order to receive. Emptiness can have many meanings.

J: Many people feel a deep emptiness within. They can find no meaning in their lives. They are burnt out.

AC: This happens in those times of life when emptiness is forced on them. If I am lonely, without a job and feeling desolate, basic elements of my life have then been taken away and I feel that something fundamental is missing. This deficiency is a sign of our times. There are many words for it: burn-out or depression or addictions or meaninglessness. There is a striking example of this kind of burn-out in the Bible. The prophet Elijah had slaved for God (see 1 Kings 19:1–13), but things go wrong and he endures a number of failures. Even his life is threatened. He sees his mission as a total failure and he suffers a breakdown. He is empty inside and completely drained. He lies down beneath a furze bush and wants to die. However, although his state is indeed desperate, his breakdown makes him receptive to a new encounter with God. Every breakdown harbours a fresh opportunity. Just when our own strength can no longer carry us, something deep within us is triggered. This can open doors that show us a way forward and allow us to sort out our lives anew.

38

J: In the context of Christian spirituality, emptiness means a voluntary self-emptying. This is what we practise in the contemplative retreat. We do not pay attention to our thoughts, our imagination, images or projects. That is to say, we let them come into our minds and we let them go again, but we do not hold on to them tightly, nor do we fight them off. If I have my hands full of things that I am holding on to, then I cannot take or receive anything else. Therefore, we are emptied of our own plans and thoughts and are open for whatever wants to show or reveal itself, for whatever wants to communicate itself.

AC: I don't think voluntary emptiness is quite as simple as that. I have often discussed with my mother the words of the prayer by the Swiss hermit, Nicholas of Flüe: 'My Lord and my God, take me from myself and make me completely yours.' She used to say: 'I cannot and do not want simply to give myself up. I want to live as well.' She had understood the prayer as a call to self-abandonment. However, it is not a matter of giving up what makes me uniquely me, but rather of letting go of any limiting ideas about myself so that I can receive life in its fullness from God. The biblical expression for this is: 'Whoever loses life for my sake will find it' (Matthew 16:25).

J: I think your mother realised something important. The call to emptiness can also go in an unhealthy direction. If I have not yet really arrived at my full potential in life and if there is much in me that has not yet been allowed to be fully alive, then the call to give something up and to become empty does not make any sense at all. First of all, something has to come to life. Only then can I also give something up. There is no problem giving something up if I can trust that God will fill my emptiness. My longing for God leads me forward. Because the word 'emptiness' is so often misunderstood, I wonder if 'receptivity' would actually be a better and more precise word?

AC: I am not so sure. It could be that something is then glossed over. When we use the word 'receptivity' another aspect immediately comes into play: that of receiving something. There is a state of emptiness when even receiving something is uncertain. It is in this state of absolute nothingness that we need to be patient, to keep going, faithful and blindly trusting. This is what our forefather Abraham went through during his wait of more than twenty-five years until the promise 'I will make of you a great nation' (Genesis 12:2) was fulfilled. In the New Testament, much is said about emptiness, often using 'poverty' as a synonym. There are more than twenty passages in which Jesus strongly invites us to embrace emptiness. I am thinking here of the number of times that Jesus invites us to sell everything, for example in the parable of the treasure in the field or of the pearl (Matthew 13:44–46), or in his comment that 'It is easier for a camel to pass through the eye of a needle than for someone rich to enter the kingdom of God' (Mark 10:25). Why does Jesus feel so strongly about this? Do you understand it?

J: Jesus looks into our heart and asks: To what is your heart attached? Is it attached to ephemeral values such as riches, possessions, success, which are all transient, or is your heart attached to what is permanent, what is always there? 'For where your treasure is, there will your heart be too' (Matthew 6:21).

AC: Is Jesus only interested in what is passing or what is permanent?

J: What he was also concerned about was the question: Am I inwardly free? Can I let everything be called into question or am I firmly fixed on certain ideas? In this context Ignatius speaks of 'indifference' in order to be inwardly free and available to the will of God. 'Indifference' means equanimity, composure, serenity, inner peace. For Ignatius it is basically a case of letting go of our attachments and fixations. He calls attachments 'disordered affections' (SE 1).

AC: Jesus' invitation for us to become empty also expresses a longing: the longing of God to give himself to us. We need an inner space for this to be possible. We create this space by practising listening into the silence and being present and alert. A contemplative retreat offers the structure and conditions to facilitate this. The external stillness is maintained by our keeping silent. This silence creates an empty space that allows room for God to work within us and communicate himself. We prepare ourselves for inward silence by practising being aware and by embracing what is there. Like an empty vessel we remain open and receptive to God's working within us in the silence.

J: That is also crucial for our interpersonal relationships. Being fixated on my own personal needs, wishes and expectations, spoils the contact I have with another and might even lead me to use the other person for my own agenda. On the other hand, if I can be completely present to the other person, then true encounter can take place.

AC: This idea of being completely present there for others reminds me of the fairy tale 'The Star-Money'. It used to impress me greatly when I was a child. It tells how a poor orphan who owned nothing apart from a piece of bread went out into the world. On the way she gives away what little she has to the needy. Then the stars fall as silver coins from the sky. The orphan is wearing a fine, new linen shift in which she catches them. I liked this attitude of giving and receiving so much that I used to lift up my own apron to the skies just like the little orphan. No silver coins fell, admittedly, but I had still understood that such a self-emptying as this, freely given, opens the heavens and draws down God's grace. As a child, this promise comforted me greatly.

J: That fairy tale does indeed convey something of the mystery of emptiness and fullness. I had a similarly intense experience when I was in India as part of my Jesuit formation. I was working at a social project for children suffering from AIDS. When it was time to leave I gave them little medallions as farewell gifts. One little girl, who was particularly poverty stricken, showed a pure and radiant joy that I had never seen in anyone before. She was complete joy. It was obvious to me that her poverty, her illness and her emptiness had made her extremely receptive to both the small and the big gifts in life.

AC: If we are honest, everyone has to walk the way of emptiness. Through self-emptying we encounter one of the laws of life: our life is finite. Death brings us face to face with the experience of a radical emptiness. It can be a helpful exercise to consider our own lives from the perspective of their transience and death so that I can recognise what is really important in my life and to what my heart is attached. Ignatius, in his Spiritual Exercises, suggests looking at things 'as if I were at the point of death' (SE 186).

J: From a Christian point of view, death itself is not the end but rather a passage into a new life. In the hymn recorded in the letter to the Philippians (Philippians 2:5–11) Jesus' death on the cross is described as a radical self-emptying. The Greek word *kenosis*, meaning 'self-emptying' or 'giving up', is used here. The radical fruit of Jesus' surrender to death is resurrection. Easter gives us a single message of encouragement to face the emptiness we experience in life in the same way as when we face it when confronted with it in death.

AC: If we take that to heart, we grow and become inwardly free. Particularly in spiritual accompaniment, time and again many different kinds of lack of freedom come to light.

J: Yes, I come across this as well. Frequently, addiction is a form of lack of freedom. It comes in many different, even subtle, forms. It is a major issue in life as well as on retreat.

AC: Addictions are an expression of an inner emptiness. They express a longing for an aliveness that cannot be achieved, and the tendency, therefore, is to fill this vacuum prematurely with false things. This leads to an inauthentic fullness, to something that cannot quell our hunger and thirst for a fulfilled life.

J: Seen like this, the self-emptying in spiritual life or on retreat could be thought of as a kind of detox: a withdrawal that is necessary and healing so that we can be free for God's purpose.

AC: I've got an example of this. I remember a retreatant who suffered from terrible boredom. To avoid this she became engrossed in many activities. Boredom was an unbearable emptiness for her. To be able to go through a process of growth, it was essential for her to withdraw from all these activities. After courageously going through a period of desolate boredom, a whole range of devastating childhood memories appeared. The boredom was obviously just a smokescreen to hide these unresolved conflicts. When these had been observed, communicated and integrated, her boredom disappeared.

J: The question for me is: How are we to differentiate a good or authentic emptiness from an inauthentic false one? Are there any criteria?

AC: I can ask myself what kind of resonance there is within me if a retreatant speaks of emptiness. I can consider how the person deals with the state of emptiness. And I can be aware of the context from which the person has come. Are they living in well-ordered circumstances? Are they coping well in life and satisfied with the way things are going? A further point to consider is how well the person knows themselves and whether or not they are able to perceive themselves realistically.

J: If a retreatant does not have a true perception of themselves or the person accompanying does not perceive them properly, it might lead to misconceptions. For example, a severe depression could be interpreted as a 'dark night', and a mental health issue would then be mistaken for a deep spiritual phase. I have come across this myself whilst accompanying people. I think everyone involved has to be attentive in order to differentiate between the two. St Ignatius calls this 'discernment of the spirits'.

AC: We have been walking quite a way with each other now. It's time for us to take a moment to pause and to reflect on the effect that the conversation has had on us. Like the disciples on the road to Emmaus we want to ask ourselves:

Where were my eyes opened?
Where was my heart burning?

J: My heart was burning at the insight that inner self-emptying is comparable in the spiritual process to a detox from things to which I am addicted.

AC: My eyes were opened when I realised that it is crucial to differentiate between a genuine emptiness and an inauthentic emptiness.

44

Exercises:
15 minutes silence

Where were my eyes opened? Where was my heart burning?
What am I attached to?

I write down three things or issues to which I am attached on three different cards. Then I imagine separating myself step by step from each of the three issues (cards) and notice what effect this has on me.

5
HEALING
AND WHOLENESS

Introduction

We are usually unaware of the close linguistic link between the words 'healing' and 'wholeness'. We can, however, be 'whole,' even without being healed of our illness, if we are connected with the core of our innermost being. With this connection, we can accept our life as it is.

Jesus says, 'The kingdom of God is among you' (Luke 17:21). Another way of translating this passage is: 'The kingdom of God is within you.' We could understand this to mean that within every person there is an inner space where we are whole and intact, not separated from, but in harmony with God. This space is like the 'treasure in the field' of our body, or like a 'pearl' at the bottom of our soul (Matthew 13:44–46). Can we really believe that? Are we really aware of it? We can often experience ourselves as separated and estranged from our own centre. We are overwhelmed, lonely and looking for healing and wholeness. The biblical interpretation is that we need healing. There are other terms for healing with which we are well acquainted – liberation, deliverance, salvation. The key questions are: How do we become whole? How do we tap into the heaven within us? The contemplative way is a way of salvation, of liberation. When we begin a journey inwards, we come into contact with our darknesses, with whatever is not 'whole' or redeemed in our lives. At the same time we discover something of immense value on the way: the treasure in the field of our soul.

Conversation

Joachim:
People frequently come to Haus Gries on retreat who are longing for healing and who sense that something fundamental is missing in their lives. Some are confronted with physical illness or illness of the soul. Annette Clara, you are a medical doctor. Have you any experience of physical problems showing themselves during the retreat that are possibly of a different origin, either psychological or spiritual?

Annette Clara:
Yes, that happens a lot.

J: Could you give me an example?

AC: I once accompanied a woman on retreat who suffered from frequent bouts of diarrhoea. Medical investigations had not found any physical disorder. During the retreat it became clear that a deep sadness within her was the cause of the diarrhoea. We were able to find a way of putting it into words: 'The bowel is weeping.' Once she was in touch with her grief, could share it and come to terms with it, the diarrhoea disappeared. She was able to recognise the reason for her grief, which was subsequently treated in psychotherapy. Our body often stores important emotions and expresses them in physical form. It is like a memory box of different experiences. It wants to assist us, especially if we cannot (yet) perceive the feelings for what they are.

J: So that means that the signals coming from our body – even the unpleasant ones – are something positive because they draw our attention to something that wants to be perceived, heard and acknowledged.

AC: Exactly. I remember a man who had tinnitus. Although he had already consulted many doctors, the tinnitus continued. Then he had a chance to change his job. In the exploratory talks the tinnitus increased quite noticeably. The man recognised that, for him, there was no point pursuing this direction any further. Listening to his tinnitus, an alarm had sounded within him and subsequently he was able to use his tinnitus to monitor his next steps.

J: I, too, have noticed that awareness of your body is often a first and very concrete way of entry into yourself. We have just considered two examples of the interaction between body and soul. In medicine there is an entire field of psychosomatics which explores this. St Paul speaks of the spirit as being a point of reference with regard to health or illness. For you, is 'spirit' the same as 'soul'?

AC: For me, spirit has to do with 'order'. It has to do with moderation. A crucial moderation seems to me to be the balance between activity and rest. It is like breathing in and out, like resting within myself and then moving into the outside world again. We need both in order to live. With regard to 'order', we have to ask the following questions: Have I got values in my life? On what do I orient myself? What meaning do I give to my life? What are my uppermost values? And, from a Christian perspective, is God in first place for me? I understand the spirit as being the ordering principle of my soul. If this order is coherent, then, as St Paul describes them in the Letter to the Galatians, the fruits of the spirit are evident: 'love, joy, peace, patience, kindness, goodness, faith, gentleness and self-control' (Galatians 5:22f).

J: It is exactly this order that makes it possible for our life energy to flow.

AC: In the gospels Jesus heals the blind, the deaf and the lame. The blind can see, the lame walk, the deaf hear. So Jesus healed them quite specifically. Could that not lead to a misunderstanding? We might only recognise healing if our physical complaints have been removed.

J: I would differentiate here between a healing that cures my illness and an experience of wholeness that makes possible a different way of coping with the illness. If we only understand these gospel stories as physical healing, we fall short of their full meaning. Healing can take place, even though the symptoms remain, insofar as that perhaps a new perspective of my illness opens up. I am thinking about a woman who, because of her illness, made a pilgrimage to Lourdes. Although her request for healing was not heard, she returned home strengthened in her faith. She had received a new way of coping with her illness.

AC: From this perspective how do you understand the healing of the blind Bartimaeus (Mark 10:46–52)?

J: Bartimaeus is sitting at the side of the road, begging. Jesus comes past and Bartimaeus calls out to him. The crowd want to silence him but Bartimaeus does not let himself be put off. He calls out even louder because he needs help and he trusts Jesus: 'Jesus, Son of David, have mercy on me.' He refuses to let his longing for healing be taken away from him. He learns to look at what is important to him and speaks up for it. This brings him into contact with Jesus. He throws his cloak off and goes towards him. The cloak could stand for what was covered or hidden in Bartimaeus. He goes out of himself and shows himself. He expresses what he desires for himself.

AC: We learn this on retreat. We put aside the cloak of our cover-up or our suppression. We look at what shows itself in our innermost being and, with that, we turn towards Jesus. We trust in the biblical verse: 'The truth will set you free' (John 8:32). Through communicating we can be healed of our blind spots and find a new way of looking at our life. These are important criteria for the process of healing within the contemplative retreat. This is why the one-to-one conversations are so important.

J: For Ignatius, it is very important that the retreatant recognises and expresses 'what I want and desire' (SE 48). This is exactly what the story about Bartimaeus illustrates so impressively. Jesus encourages him with the question: 'What do you want me to do for you?'

AC: It isn't quite so simple. I am reminded of a man who was suffering from cancer and already had a lot of metastases. Of course he wanted God to heal him and asked: 'Can I trust in God's love? Will he heal me if I pray a lot?'

J: Just because we desire something does not mean that God will fulfil our desire in the way we would like. Dietrich Bonhoeffer articulated it in this way: 'God does not fulfil all our desires, but all his promises.' From a Christian perspective healing is a gift from God, not ours to control. We are touching here on the age-old question that plagued Job in the Old Testament: Is there any point to suffering and illness?

AC: Thinking back to accompanying that terminally ill man, I realise that I was confronted with my own vulnerability when faced with his fate and his questions. The fact that I didn't run away but stayed there, neither mollifying nor glossing over anything, was a consoling and healing experience for him.

J: What actually makes us ill?

AC: What particularly occurs to me here is the way people are reduced to performance and efficiency combined with extreme pressure and speed. In addition to this, we are flooded every-where with images and information. There are too few places where we can simply just rest and be, without any agenda, without anyone expecting anything of us, places where we have time to find ourselves, to feel ourselves. Many people who come to us on retreat long for peace and quiet, for not having to function all the time. They do not want to be seen only as resources but as individuals. Yet in the retreats, and in contrast to medicine, our primary and ultimate aim is not healing. We are seeking an encounter with the God who heals, not healing itself. If that happens, it is a fortuitous side effect.

J: My impression is that many people allow themselves this time out only if they are sick. Ignatius was confined to bed for months after being seriously injured in battle. His career as an officer had ended in one stroke. He had to rethink all his ideas and his plan for life completely. His illness gave him the time for it and for the first time brought him into contact with deeper levels within himself. This led him to turn his life around and give it a totally new direction. It is quite clear here how illness can also offer new opportunities. Do you think there are any illnesses that are typical of the present day?

AC: Yes, indeed. There is an increase in cardiovascular diseases, such as heart attacks, high blood pressure and strokes. These all reflect that we often live under high pressure and so the natural circulation of life has become severely disordered. Another area is the increase in mental health issues, such as burn-out, sleep disorders and depression.

J: Ignatius sees the aim of the retreat as the 'orientation on God, a new ordering of life and salvation of the soul' (SE 1). We have already spoken occasionally about the difference between healing and salvation/wholeness. Do you think there is another difference between healing and wholeness?

AC: Yes. To my mind, healing belongs primarily in the area of medicine. If somebody has gallstones and these are removed, then he is healed of his suffering. Wholeness, on the other hand, touches a spiritual dimension in my life and could be translated as 'being at peace', 'at one with myself and my life', with or without illness. The biblical word *shalom* (peace, wholeness) expresses this in a comprehensive way.

J: In the healing stories of the New Testament, healing and wholeness happen together.

AC: Yes, but there is hidden danger there as well. If we read and understand the stories of healing as meaning only a physical healing, then we will often be disappointed when our desire for healing from a physical illness is not answered. If I learn to accept my illness I can experience healing or wholeness. It is this interior freedom to face being either healthy or sick that Ignatius refers to in the Principle and Foundation (SE 23) of his Spiritual Exercises when he speaks of being open to poverty or riches, health or sickness, and facing both with equanimity.

J: Is that what you mean by holistic healing or becoming whole?

AC: Yes, it's linked to that. I don't focus on a particular problem or a symptom on which the whole of my life's happiness depends but rather I discover an inner space where I am at one with myself and my life. The way there is like a journey inwards. The retreat is a well-tried path for this. The Flemish mystic Jan Ruysbroeck says: 'We go towards God from the outside inwards, and God comes towards us from the inside outwards.'

J: Medicine and various psychotherapeutic schools have also discovered the spiritual dimension as a healing factor. 'Spiritual care' is the expression for this new branch within medical research and therapy. One psychoanalyst notes that at the beginning of a therapy he asks the patient about their religious resources and experience. This has become standard practice for him. From experience he knows that this dimension can alleviate the illness and improve the prospect of healing.

AC: Particularly when we are on retreat, the spiritual dimension has priority. It is not for nothing that doctors are beginning to recommend a guided retreat as a form of therapeutic time out. Nevertheless, there is a difference with the spiritual care approach. We do not use this dimension in order to aim for specific results or to alleviate symptoms. In our focus on God we are without aims or goals. We come before God with an attitude of inner freedom. This does not mean that I have no intentions but it means that I have an inner freedom concerning how my intentions are fulfilled. St Ignatius describes this as indifference, which for him means the same as 'freedom of Spirit'.

AC: We have been walking quite a way with each other now. It's time for us to take a moment to pause and to reflect on the effect that the conversation has had on us. Like the disciples on the road to Emmaus we want to ask ourselves:

Where were my eyes opened?
Where was my heart burning?

AC: My eyes were opened at the insight that the biblical stories of healing mean far more than just a treatment of individual symptoms. For me, they show how crucial it is to change our inner attitudes if we are to become whole.

J: My heart was burning at the insight that the Spirit wants to prepare the way for life to the full. The Spirit is the ordering principle in a holistic process of healing. Spiritual exercises create a space in which the Spirit can work.

Exercises: 15 minutes silence

Where were my eyes opened whilst I was reading? Where was my heart burning?

What are the routines in my life that are healthy?

What fresh adjustment is needed in my life?

6
SUFFERING AND CONSOLATION

Introduction

One criticism often aimed at Christians is the one-sided way they apparently focus on suffering. There seems to be, therefore, little or no space for joy and vitality. The priority of a God of love could surely not be to condemn humankind to suffer as much as possible, and GOOD News could by no means be the call to carry the cross.

However, our experience from accompanying people on contemplative retreats shows that suffering – living through pain, bitterness or issues with which we are not reconciled – is indeed a way that frees, heals and consoles us and leads us to new life. Suffering and pain are part of the human condition. Trying to avoid this part of reality or being overwhelmed by it results in our not being free. We remain bound to pain. The contemplative way wants to teach us a way of dealing with suffering and pain that leads to freedom and to joy.

Conversation

Joachim:
'Anyone who wants to be a follower of mine, must renounce self and take up the cross every day and follow me' (Luke 9:23). Does being a Christian mean suffering and does it mean having little self-esteem?

Annette Clara:
By no means. Any suffering in our external life that we can avoid, we should indeed avoid or alleviate and seek to heal. It is certainly not a matter of accepting everything problematic that life throws at me. Rather it is remaining in an attitude of awareness, checking whether or not it is a matter that needs to be addressed or to be accepted. I need to make a clear decision: Am I or am I not going into a difficult situation or a conflict? This is what Jesus did. Sometimes he avoided conflict, such as in his visit to Nazareth (Luke 4:30). It is not a matter of looking for suffering but rather accepting and bearing the suffering that life demands of us with our eyes firmly fixed on Jesus. When he speaks about discipleship, Jesus refers to the way we already have of coping with suffering in our lives. In the middle of our suffering he invites us to come into a closer relationship with him, to look at him and to let ourselves be looked at by him.

J: And the 'renouncing of self'?

AC: We do not want to suffer. What Jesus is saying is that we should strengthen our willingness to face this painful dimension of life rather than following through on our first knee-jerk reaction to avoid suffering and pain whenever possible.

J: With regard to this, Ignatius's concept of *agere contra* – acting against – comes to mind. By this, Ignatius means the freedom to act contrary to our first inclinations and impulses. Anyone who practises *agere contra* feels how it enables a space for new experiences and growth to open up. It is an important principle to help us break free from old patterns and habits and to venture into new territory. If we are, for example, fixated on always having agreeable feelings, then we are inwardly not free.

AC: I think that one of the main aims of the 'wellness' trend is to avoid pain. It is exactly this, however, that makes us dependent on feeling good or else dependent on people who promise that our lives can be pain-free. But life and pain belong together. We see this in the people we accompany on contemplative retreats. This is why some people are afraid of making retreats. They say: 'I am not going on retreat because I feel overwhelmed already and I don't know what kind of painful issue might emerge.' What would you say to them?

J: I would tell them that there can indeed be phases during the retreat when people seemingly feel worse rather than better. But the perspective of the retreat is towards healing. Even a doctor sometimes has to perform painful interventions in order to heal a person. That is the opportunity of such experiences. In the silence, the prayer, the community and the personal accompaniment an atmosphere can evolve that allows trust. All can surface, even what is painful in my life. What has been put on ice, interiorly speaking, can be warmed in this atmosphere and thaw. I would tell them that retreats show a way to find consolation in suffering because we are turning ourselves towards God who lets us experience 'I am here for you.'

AC: I once experienced this profoundly when I was going through a situation of bullying from which I could see no escape. In my desperation I turned to a priest who said the following words to me: 'Your dignity comes from God.' It was only one sentence but it gave me support, inner orientation and strength to go through this troubled situation. The temptation to move into action, to fight and to argue, was great, particularly as I know that fighting and going into action can sometimes be necessary. In this case, it was a matter of checking within myself and being aware of what I needed to do at that moment. It was quite clear to me that at that point in time I should not move into doing anything but simply trust. This means I should just be aware of what is there and let God take over the controls. And that is what God did. After a few months a door opened to a new career opportunity that fulfilled me and in which I could better develop my talents.

J: It seems to me that apart from what the priest said that gave you direction, it was also important that you were able to talk to and share about it with another person.

AC: Yes, that was very important for me.

J: In sharing, something significant often happens. Something is brought into the relationship to the person sitting opposite me. This is what is so valuable about spiritual accompaniment during retreats. There is somebody there who listens to me, who sees me and takes me as I am. I am not alone in my pain. In this relationship something can be seen. This is well expressed by the Latin word *consolatio*, meaning 'to be *with* someone who is *solo*, alone'. Consolation is an experience of being *with* someone.

AC: Just how important it is to have someone there, in relationship with you, when you are in pain, is seen in Jesus' prophecy of his Passion in Matthew 16:13–23. Jesus asks Peter: 'Who am I for you? How do you see me?' Peter answers; 'You are the Christ, the Son of the living God.' Jesus feels that he has been recognised and opens himself up further by proposing that he will have to suffer. Peter rejects this vehemently: 'This must not happen to you!' In other words, suffering should or must be avoided at any cost. I can imagine just how much that hurt Jesus because the strong rebuke that follows – 'Get behind me, Satan!' – shows that a confidential closeness has suddenly become a yawning gap. Not understood, Jesus is left alone with his pain. He cannot share openly with anyone. This is also true of us when we are not allowed to show our pain. We cannot experience any consolation and we cannot grow.

J: This is where contemplative retreats come into their own. They give us space to come into contact with our pain. We go into silence, focus ourselves on the presence of God and allow everything to be there that wants to reveal itself to us. This is what being aware means: taking what is there as my truth. Looking at it honestly it is important to see if issues with which we have not yet come to terms, or which have hurt us, are revealing themselves. Suppressing our pain or looking for ways of avoiding it takes energy and creates new suffering.

AC: I remember a man who came on a contemplative retreat and told me in the first one-to-one conversation: I am at peace with myself. I know my feelings and I have worked through my life story. He sat there motionless, a barely perceptible expression on his face. During the retreat he became more in touch with the life within him and this brought him into contact with violent rage and bitterness. He had needed a space where these feelings could be there, without being evaluated or analysed. Bit by bit that gave him inner freedom, energy and growing joy.

J: Your example shows that the contemplative way can bring us into a more sensitive contact with ourselves. If we sense that something unpleasant is rising from within us, we can renew our willingness to let everything be there. We don't occupy ourselves with our feelings, nor do we want to analyse them or try actively to change them. Nor do we allow ourselves to be sucked into the whirlpool of our emotions. We are simply aware of our emotions; we feel them, and with them we turn to the present moment and to the healing presence of God. Our feelings are like children who are welcomed, integrated and lovingly embraced, just as we are in the comforting presence of a mother or a close friend.

AC: Have you got a personal example from your life for that?

J: Yes, something that happened to me when I was a child comes to mind. When I was five years old, I went to a fair with my mother and my aunt. The festival tent was packed full of people and in the melee I lost sight of my mother and aunt. All I could see were the legs of strangers and I panicked. The situation was emotionally totally overwhelming for me. I stood there as if nailed to the ground. One of the adults standing nearby noticed this and took me to the stage at the front. He asked the conductor of the festival band to make an announcement: 'Here is a little boy who has lost his mother.' When my mother came to the stage and put her arms round me, my numbness dissolved. I could cry and the feelings that I had kept back could flow and I could be comforted in my mother's arms.

AC: It seems as if pain in itself is not the worst thing. It is far worse to be left on our own with our pain, not knowing where we can go or to whom we can turn.

J: The contemplative way shows us that, in our pain, we can turn to the comforting presence of God. It also shows us how to do it. That is GOOD News, after all.

AC: Precisely. Even pain has many positive traits. It shows us the fracture points where development was blocked. Pain makes us aware that there is something there that needs attention. Seen like this, pain opens us up for relationship and also for growth where it hurts. When Jesus invites us to take our cross upon ourselves and at the same time to look at HIM, new life can be given to us. This is a promise of Easter in the midst of daily life. Ignatius talks about this in his Spiritual Exercises in the Fourth Week, when he speaks of the resurrection and when he speaks of Jesus being the consoler: 'Consider the office of consoler which Christ our Lord carries out and compare it with the way friends console one another' (SE 224).

J: We have been walking quite a way with each other now. It's time for us to take a moment to pause and to reflect on the effect that the conversation has had on us. Like the disciples on the road to Emmaus we want to ask ourselves:

Where were my eyes opened?
Where was my heart burning?

AC: I have seen Jesus' call to carry the cross in discipleship in a new light: as GOOD News and as an Easter promise. Any pain or suffering that is suffered through in relationship with Christ and by gazing at Christ leads to new life.

J: My heart was burning at the insight that Christian suffering is comforted suffering. We can turn to our resurrected Lord, who is always and everywhere right at our side.

Exercises:
15 minutes silence

Where were my eyes opened? Where was my heart burning?

I think back to a situation when I felt that I was left alone with and in my pain. I ask myself: What did I need at that time?

I recall a situation when I was comforted in my pain. What led to my being able to experience comfort in my pain?

I ask myself: In my prayer do I allow myself to acknowledge pain?

7
FORGIVENESS
AND RECONCILIATION

Introduction

Making a public confession has become fashionable on many talk shows nowadays. Getting things off your chest appears to be sorely needed. Yet it is not enough just to share with someone else in order to be freed of old burdens. In our Christian tradition we are well acquainted with a path that can and wants to lead us to a healing experience. Forgiveness is Jesus' heartfelt desire and it is at the centre of our Christian faith, for God wants us to live. When we cannot forgive, life dies within us. For example, if we no longer want to have any contact with a certain person because they have hurt us and we cannot forgive that person, then we might say: '(S)he is dead to me.' However, if we forgive or experience forgiveness, then life can flow again and relationships can be restored to life. There is a difference between forgiveness and reconciliation. Forgiveness marks the beginning of the healing process and complete reconciliation is the end of this process.

forgive

Conversation

Annette Clara:
We want to talk about the topic of forgiveness and reconciliation. I would like to begin by looking at the end of Jesus' life. The way in which somebody dies tells us a lot about his life. The last words of a dying person have a special meaning for us. Among Jesus' last words were: 'Father forgive them, for they do not know what they are doing' (Luke 23:34). How do you understand this?

Joachim:
Jesus gets to the heart of the matter with these words. People are driven by unconscious forces. They don't see the evil that they are doing. They are not their own masters. They have lost their compassion for other people. Jesus sees each individual in his or her misery and lack of freedom, and he has compassion.

AC: I can't go along with all of that yet. What about the people who utterly intentionally do wrong? People who deliberately cause damage, for example, by libel, betrayal or the many kinds of violence. Are these evil deeds, consciously committed, excluded from Jesus' prayer of forgiveness?

J: By no means. Jesus' prayer includes forgiveness for both unconsciously and consciously committed wrongs. Inviting us to 'love your enemies' (Matthew 5:44), Jesus also challenges us quite radically to love those people who quite deliberately want to hurt us. Jesus doesn't seem to be describing a superficial 'let's forget it and be buddies' mentality. For Jesus, love and forgiveness are always linked to truth and justice. It is clear from the way in which Jesus addresses his prayer to the Father that the power to for-

66

give comes from being focused on God. Jesus is one who fights for truth and justice – but he does so with a reconciled heart.

AC: That means, too, that I should not exonerate the injustice done to me or that I do to others, but rather that I should be aware of it and also accept the suffering involved. I can only reconcile myself with what I have become aware of and have lovingly 'suffered through'. This means that I am prepared to suffer whatever causes me pain until it no longer hurts. This is when the heart softens. On the other hand, everything that we cannot forgive leaves behind resentment or hardness within us. God's summary, which he expresses through the prophet Ezekiel, is that humankind has a 'heart of stone' (Ezekiel 36:26).

J: Yes, softening our hearts is an important attitude. At first it characterises our way of coping with a hurt within us, but then it affects our way of coping with external situations too. Sometimes it can be important, however, in our conduct with others, to make clear where our limits are, to draw the line or else to confront somebody. As long as confronting someone does not come from an inner hardheartedness, then conflicts can be resolved a better way.

AC: Forgiveness is more than a one-off for Jesus. When I think of Peter asking Jesus: 'How often must I forgive my brother or my sister who wrongs me?' (Matthew 18:21), it is clear that he has already understood a lot and he knows that forgiveness is close to his Master's heart. He makes a suggestion to Jesus: 'As often as seven times?' Jesus answers: 'Not seven, I tell you, but seventy-seven times' (Matthew 18:22), which is more or less saying an infinite number of times. From Jesus' perspective, forgiveness is a way of life.

J: Not only that, Jesus encourages us to keep taking the first steps towards reconciliation. He encourages us not to wait until the other approaches us first. In the Our Father we pray: 'Forgive us our trespasses as we forgive those who trespass against us.' The text in Matthew 6:12 says: 'And forgive us our debts, as we *have* forgiven our debtors.' We need to be the ones who take the first step towards reconciliation, if we are to remain free and independent of other people's behaviour. It is up to me to do my bit towards forgiveness. Even if the other person does not want to be reconciled with me, I can nevertheless find reconciliation within myself. Thinking of this, Nelson Mandela comes to mind. When asked why he had forgiven his enemies who had him put in prison, he answered: 'So that they no longer had any power over me.'

AC: For me, the 'forgive us' in the Our Father is so meaningful. We are all people with our weaknesses and imperfections. We hurt and are hurt. The whole of humankind is in the same boat when it comes to the matter of forgiveness. We need forgiveness and we are also called upon to forgive others.

J: If we cannot forgive, then we stay locked in a difficult situation. We are captive to our feelings. This is what Eli Wiesel, a Holocaust survivor, expressed so aptly. If he had not forgiven the concentration camp guards, he would have remained a prisoner of that system of injustice until he died, despite having been liberated long before that. People like Mandela or Wiesel certainly went on a long journey to reconciliation, but we do not hear how they made it there. So the question remains: How does reconciliation occur?

AC: Reconciliation is a process. The first step begins with my becoming aware that something within me hurts, something is not reconciled. This means recognising that there are things in my life with which I am not at peace. Simply admitting that can already take away a lot of inner pressure. The second step is to have the intention of forgiving. I can say inwardly: 'I would like to forgive this person.' Then it is important to see that despite this desire, our feelings of disappointment, annoyance, anger and resentment have not yet changed. We do not need to change or to evaluate these feelings, either. They can be allowed to be just as they are. We let the pain continue and, by focusing on God who wants to heal and reconcile us, we 'suffer through it' until it stops hurting. The power to forgive comes from God. It is sufficient for us to want to forgive, if that is our sincere intention.

J: This emotional 'suffering through' in the healing presence of God is the third step of reconciliation. If it is bypassed, then the liberating power of reconciliation cannot be experienced. Not being able to forgive is one of the greatest obstacles on the spiritual journey. Whoever cannot forgive lays heavy sandbags, so to speak, on his or her soul. Forgiveness itself is a handing over and emptying out of these sandbags. By doing this, we gain lightness and freedom on our spiritual journey. It is comparable to the ascent of a balloon during a balloon flight.

AC: Contemplative prayer, especially, is a path that can help us here. It brings us into contact with our unreconciled feelings, with deep pain, with resentment and anger, vulnerability, animosity. Contemplative prayer is like an X-ray. We focus on the presence of God and in so doing let HIS light fall on our life. The inner contours of hardening, of blockages, become perceivable. Perhaps the 'first week' of Ignatius's Spiritual Exercises could be seen as a similar X-ray. It considers our human weaknesses and errors in the forgiving light of God. At the end of the 'first week', celebrating the Sacrament of Reconciliation offers a ritual of forgiveness. It opens the door for the ongoing process towards reconciliation.

69

J: Whilst accompanying people on retreat, some of the main issues that recur are deep hurts from childhood, conflict with parents or siblings, painful experiences in school, conflict at work, in marriage, with the Church, and the after-effects of war through flight and displacement. The closer that people are to me, for example my parents, the deeper the hurt can often be. In such cases the path to reconciliation frequently needs considerable time.

AC: Which is why it is important not to put yourself or anyone else under pressure. I remember a lady who came to me for spiritual accompaniment during a contemplative retreat. After she and her husband had got divorced all three of her children broke off contact with her. She had no contact with them for over twenty years. Not one word was exchanged between the mother and her children during this time. Her letters remained unanswered. She suffered greatly from this estrangement and noticed that her own attempts were having no success. Confronted with her own powerlessness, the direction of her focus changed and she turned inwards. She began practising contemplative prayer and faced all her pain and her anger. After several retreats her heart gradually softened and she was able to forgive her children interiorly. She was able to accept the situation as it was and became free with regard to the way her children behaved towards her.

J: Whoever can forgive, finds peace in life. This was brought home to me powerfully when I was doing a practical in a care home. In one of the rooms there were two old women, one of whom was very embittered and often reacted irritably and aggressively. The staff in the care home didn't like dealing with her. The other woman, however, radiated benevolence and was at peace with herself. The women had had similar experiences. They had both lived through the war and had both experienced the loss of many people. There are enormous consequences for peace in my life which depend on whether or not I have travelled the path of reconciliation.

AC: What is true for the individual is also true for every community. The whole world is suffering from problems and stories from the past where there is no reconciliation. The wars throughout the history of humanity highlight the centrality of this problem. Retaliation is practised. Like a dam, what is not forgiven and reconciled restricts the natural flow of love. If people could manage to open the locks of this dam just once, then something really magnificent could happen. I am thinking here of Gandhi, for whom the Sermon on the Mount was groundbreaking. As a single individual, he led India to freedom; or Martin Luther King, who opposed the hate of apartheid with his dream of love and freedom. Such people are like lighthouses because the enormous power that comes from forgiveness is particularly visible in them.

J: These examples make it clear that there is no alternative for getting out of the spiral of hate and violence other than through forgiveness. Victims can soon become perpetrators if they have not found a way of accessing the power of forgiving. The process of reconciliation, on the part of the victim, has to correspond to the process of remorse on the part of the perpetrator. Both processes, taken together, are a recognition and a 'suffering through' of the wrong committed.

AC: There is something else I want to say about the power that comes from forgiveness. Normal proportions are suspended in the divine mathematics of forgiveness – we should forgive not seven times, but seventy-seven times. One individual can change the world through a forgiving heart. Jesus' suffering on the cross in love and forgiveness is the most powerful sign of this. His forgiving opens heaven and God's power is revealed in Jesus' resurrection from the dead. His forgiving on the cross has freed all of humanity. Forgiveness is a Paschal event because it brings new life.

J: We have been walking quite a way with each other now. It's time for us to take a moment to pause and to reflect on the effect that the conversation has had on us. Like the disciples on the road to Emmaus we want to ask ourselves:

Where were my eyes opened?
Where was my heart burning?

AC: My heart was burning when I realised just what power comes from forgiveness – a transforming power that brings peace and renews our lives.

J: My eyes were opened at the insight that there is no alternative to forgiveness for us and that we always have the freedom to take the first step.

Exercises:
15 minutes silence

Where was my heart burning whilst I was reading this?
Where were my eyes opened?

Do I have a relationship in which I could take the first step towards reconciliation?

Is there an example in my life of where I have experienced forgiveness? How has it affected my life?

8
VOCATION
AND MISSION

Introduction

The contemplative path can lead us into our vocation and mission. The most important, fundamental attitude that we practise is listening. It is only when listening that we can be aware of the inner voice, God's call. The word 'vocation' comes from the Latin vocare, meaning 'to call upon, to summon'. Through the process of listening, we can actively respond in a way in which God's will and our innermost being are in harmony. Sometimes our ears are blocked by the cacophony of our noisy times or because of unresolved inner conflicts. This is when external silence is necessary. We need a space where everything that is in us and wants to come to light can reveal itself. The contemplative path unblocks, so to speak, our ears. We experience who we are and what we are here for. It is a path into the centre of life. The signposts pointing towards vocation and mission are vitality, energy, serenity, equanimity, gratitude, joy and love, together with interpersonal skills.

Conversation

Joachim:
Annette Clara, what do you understand by vocation and mission? Do these two words have different meanings? How are they connected?

Annette Clara:
Vocation and mission are both religious terms. They are, however, relevant for everybody. The questions they ask are the fundamental ones of humanity: Who am I? What is my place in life? What can I do? What is my identity? How do I find my own way? Vocation is a sort of starting point for mission. First of all I have to be at home with myself. I have to know what I am and who I am. If I know myself and my talents, and if I can feel my longings, then I have aids to point me towards my mission. Mission, then, is the unfolding of my vocation expressed through the practical tasks and assignments in my life. It is not always possible for us to unfold to the full our potential because, for example, our family situation or the demands of work might limit us. If this is the case, then we have to be aware of and to use the spaces, there in our daily life, where we can be more open, however insignificant they might appear.

J: This reminds me of what happens with a desert palm tree. At first it grows downwards for two years until its roots have reached groundwater. There is no growth visible on the outside. I think this corresponds to the process of vocation. To begin with it is a matter of exploring and discovering my inner being. On this journey, I get to know myself. Self-experience and becoming myself are foremost. Then the palm grows upwards. This corresponds to my active move into mission. Annette Clara, have you had anything like a vocational experience in your life?

AC: Yes, I have. After many years when I had nothing to do with the Church, a single word caused me to return. During Lent one year I wanted to start a project called 'Fasting with your car' together with the local Catholic church. Talking with the priest in charge about it, we also touched briefly on more personal topics. I told him: 'You know, I go my own way with my faith. I meditate in silence. I don't need anything else.' The priest answered: 'That is very good. We should all go into our private room when we pray. That is the Spirit. The community of believers, on the other hand, is the Body.' That word 'Body' resonated gently and profoundly within me and changed my life. It was as if the word was calling me, and then, step by step, its effect unfolded. It did so in two ways. I learned to become aware of myself in a more sensitive way and at the same time I felt drawn towards community. I grew into the parish community almost automatically: Sunday service, involvement in the parish council, reader and Eucharistic minister, leading prayer groups. And what about you? Have you had a vocational experience like this?

J: When I was seventeen years old, I read a book by the Jesuit, Lassalle, about meditation. I immediately tried out what I had read and sat down to meditate. In one of these meditation times I became aware of myself quite intensively. It was the experience: 'I am here.' From then on, quietly, almost without my realising it, my life took a different course. It took years after that for what had flickered to life then to deepen. It was a journey into my own presence. Over time, the aspect of mission was added to it. I sensed the desire to help other people come to themselves and to experience the presence of God.

AC: Steps towards maturity and to the clarification of vocation and mission need time and a structure. This is why retreats are particularly helpful on the journey of discovering our own vocation and mission. Contemplative prayer can be a precious aid on this journey. We stay faithful to our practice of staying in the present moment until it becomes clear what has to be done or what has to be put aside. In our daily life we are often under the pressure of time. Hardly do we perceive something than we begin to analyse and then move into action. Sometimes this means that we make decisions too hastily instead of taking the time and patience that is often necessary.

J: Even when I was younger, I used to take my time. For many years I did not know what career I should pursue. I only knew what I didn't want to be. It was not easy for me to be so aware of the uncertainty, yet also openness, within me. I did not know what the way forward was. I often used to go on long walks, and allowed myself to feel whatever was within me, what was bothering me as well as what was invigorating me. I let it all just be there, even my helplessness. Over a period of time something changed and little by little I recognised small steps that I could take and which felt right and finally I found my way.

AC: This shows just how vocation and mission are a living process. It seems important to me that, in our lives, we remain constantly alert and listening. We also need to accept that God is a God of surprises. That reminds me of what happened to Abraham. When he was seventy-five years old, he set out yet again. Instead of being settled in his retirement, he was very willing to listen. He was so alert that he did not miss his mission call. This attitude is one that we really need to take to heart.

J: You have experienced that yourself!

76

AC: True. When I was fifty-six I started out all over again, giving up a really good position and good friends. Everything had seemed to be fine, but, nevertheless, there was a restlessness within me, something that was unfulfilled. I was not able to utilise explicitly my spiritual side in my work. People kept telling me that I should use my talents more, or even completely, in the field of spirituality. Finally I was asked if I could imagine taking up a place on a leadership team at the retreat house, Haus Gries. That was a further confirmation for me that I should take a different career path.

J: I find it interesting that you did not ignore your restlessness and dissatisfaction. This seems to me to be of general significance. Everything that becomes apparent needs first to be perceived and taken seriously. Being aware means, of course, taking what is there in the present moment to be the truth. This being the case, I can let myself be confronted with fundamental questions: Am I satisfied with my life? Do I have the feeling of being in the right place at the right time? If I can say 'yes' to my life as it is right now, then I am living my vocation and mission. This is true for all areas and challenges in life.

AC: Yes, precisely. I remember a barber who loved his job and went about it with great joy and commitment. His contentment radiated outwards and people liked going to him. If I am dissatisfied, and if I am looking for the purpose of my life, then clarifying the uncertainty about my vocation and mission would seem to be crucial. Is there anything important in my life that wants to be seen or that has not yet been lived or still lies undiscovered? Perhaps something has developed in my life in the meantime but I have yet to take the necessary steps leading to change.

J: It is at times like this we especially need time as well as someone there to listen to us and with whom we can talk things over. This might be a mother or a father, friends, a spiritual companion or a therapist. If bigger decisions need to be made, time out is important. Guided retreats are useful. They enable me to get in touch with myself and my longings and to pursue my questions in an accompanied setting. In this way I can look at my life and, oriented on God, consider what my next steps might be.

AC: Even unforeseen times, such as illness or crises at work, can be opportunities. They open up a space for a person that allows them to stand back from their normal circumstances. In this way space is made for questions about how to shape one's life. I have experienced this myself. After finishing my studies I worked at a doctor's practice. I was unhappy there because the way the patients were treated by no means corresponded to how I thought they should be treated. I had an identity crisis. This paved the way for a very rewarding change in my professional life.

J: 'Crisis' is a good cue. The biblical stories of vocation and mission are usually connected with crises. The prophet, Moses, for example (Exodus 2–4), had to flee Egypt and begin completely anew on Mount Sinai. After he had been tending sheep there for many years, the inner ground of his soul had been prepared for the encounter with the burning bush. Through this he could experience who he was and what his mission was to be: to lead the Israelites from foreign rule in Egypt into their own country. The case of Moses highlights another aspect, namely, the connection between my weakness and my vocation and mission. Moses was not a great orator but he was sent to convince Pharaoh, through speech, to let the Israelites go.

AC: People are often under the impression that they are not the right one for a specific task. This needs to be examined carefully. Being aware of our vulnerabilities, in particular, can be all important in pointing us in the direction of our vocation and mission. By mastering difficulties we develop strengths that enable us to perform certain tasks. This link becomes clear in the story about a palm tree with a stone in its crown. The stone was put onto it to weigh it down so that the palm tree would form a particularly strong trunk. This strong trunk enabled the tree to bear heavy weight more easily.

J: This reminds me of an author I once accompanied on a contemplative retreat. Past hurts caused him to ask: 'Can I make myself understood? Am I being understood?' This deep desire to be understood motivated him early in life to strive to express himself carefully and precisely.

His talent today is exactly this: he can express complex issues in an easily understandable way.

AC: Yes, your example of the author shows that finding my mission in life is not a purely personal affair. It has a wide effect on other people and on the world about us too. I think that the questions 'Who am I?' 'Why am I here?' are inseparably interwoven with considerations for the community. As human beings we are relational creatures. If we find our place and our calling in life, then this has an impact on the community around us. We are in a vibrant, reciprocal relationship. What has matured on an interior level in the individual, wants to be lived out in the community. This living out has, in turn, its own effect on the individual. It brings about a vitality in the individual as well as benefits to the community. Jesus sends his disciples out in twos. We can see this as a sign of the interconnection between vocation, mission and community.

J: We have been walking quite a way with each other now. It's time for us to take a moment to pause and to reflect on the effect that the conversation has had on us. Like the disciples on the road to Emmaus we want to ask ourselves:

Where were my eyes opened?
Where was my heart burning?

J: As a result of our conversation I have realised just how closely linked vocation and mission are. They are like two sides of the same coin. The memory of my own vocation has also made it clear how closely this experience is linked with my present assignment and mission. I came to know myself through contemplative prayer. Now, as director of a retreat house, I accompany many people on their journey in practising contemplative prayer.

AC: As a result of our conversation I realise that the many hurts and weaknesses of our lives can be pointers with regard to vocation and mission. What I will take to heart is two things. One is the importance of asking, especially at the beginning of an accompaniment in a retreat or spiritual direction context, if anything significantly disturbing has happened during a person's life. The second is the awareness that out of such difficulties, strengths can emerge.

Exercises:
15 minutes silence

Where were my eyes opened whilst I was reading this?
Where was my heart burning?

Have I had a vocation experience in my life? A particular
word calling me?

Can I name a past hurt in my life?

Has there been any growth towards vocation and mission
through this past hurt?

9
JESUS
THE MASTER

Introduction

Many people set out for far-off countries in search of a spiritual master. We encounter statues of Buddha in doctors' practices, gardens, shop windows etc. Interest in the religions and mysticism of the Far East is booming: Buddhism, Hinduism, Sufism. There are many places where courses on these subjects are available. If we speak with course participants about Christianity we can often be met with scepticism. It is as if they think no deep mystical journey can be found in Christianity. Yet Christianity has a rich tradition of mystical experience and depth. In his Spiritual Exercises, Ignatius of Loyola gave clear instructions about how we can prepare ourselves for an encounter with the Master. We can also think about the Desert Fathers, or about the great mystics such as John of the Cross or Teresa of Avila who, in their writings and from their own experience, all describe the spiritual journey to their master, Jesus Christ.

Conversation

Joachim:
A lot of people are looking for a master or a guru who can give their life orientation. Why do you think this is?

Annette Clara:
Obviously they haven't found their master yet! In the midst of a highly coordinated world, many people are looking for spaces of silence as well as for a meaning to their lives. I think another driving force for this search seems to be the longing for health and freedom from pain. Some people hope that a master will supply some kind of recipe that will enable them to go through life happily and free of care.

J: Some hope that there is someone who will relieve them from doing work on themselves. Just as a doctor is supposed to remove the symptoms of an illness, they think this master should remove all the difficulties in their life. Working on oneself, however, demands courage and cannot be delegated. Jesus does not save us from this work.

AC: Jesus takes us into his school so that we can learn his skills and become 'master students'. His training programme includes self-knowledge, love of truth, patience and trust. It is especially the work we do on ourselves that enables us to be there for others. Equipped with these skills, we can also overcome difficult situations in our own lives. I have noticed that those coming on our retreats are often people from the caring professions. They sense that they can help others only if they come to the source of their own lives themselves, by turning time and again to their master, Jesus. What is it that makes Jesus a 'master' for you?

J: His life is so totally authentic. Whatever he says or does is consistent and it has a liberating effect on other people. Jesus loved the truth. I am impressed by his autonomy. He went through life, head uplifted, and did not allow himself to be diverted from his path. It is quite obvious that he lived out of a deep relationship with God. I want to mention two significant passages: his baptism in the Jordan (Luke 3:21f), in which he experiences himself as the 'beloved Son', and the Transfiguration on Mount Tabor (Matthew 17:1–9), where he is confirmed again as the 'beloved Son'. For me, Jesus is the greatest master.

AC: Jesus was indeed shown to be a special person at his baptism in the Jordan. But that did not make a master of him. Like every master, he had to take his master's test. He did that in the desert where the Spirit led him immediately after his baptism (Luke 4:1–13). This is where he encountered the shadows of human existence and had to face them himself. Three temptations are recounted with particular emphasis given to the temptation of narcissistic self-appointed authority. Each of the different forms of temptation that Jesus encountered locks into the weak points of humanity. He suffered hunger, vulnerability, depression and the feeling of nothingness. At this time his whole person is being challenged. He passes this test – his master's test – by his clear orientation on his Father through prayer and by words spoken from Scripture. His authorisation comes from God. He begins his mission and public ministry as master with the calling of his first disciples.

J: The disciples gradually get to know Jesus in a deeper way. They experience him on Mount Tabor (Luke 9:28–36) quite clearly as an enlightened master. Jesus, his true being and his divine Sonship shine between the great prophets Moses and Elijah. The disciples want to hold on to this extraordinary experience and build huts, but Jesus is not prepared to go along with this proposal of setting himself up in comfort on Mount Tabor. He shows himself to be very down-to-earth. He calls upon the disciples to go back down into everyday life. He also tells them of his suffering to come. For Jesus, the authenticity of a spiritual peak experience is the way it is proved in everyday life with its joys and suffering. Both of these can be seen together in the Beatitudes of the Sermon on the Mount (Matthew 5:3–12).

AC: Jesus stands with both feet on the ground. True masters do not hold on to particular experiences but teach a spirituality that is grounded in everyday life. They lead people to become independent. Inauthentic masters, on the other hand, rely for their self-esteem on the admiration and affirmation of the people who come to them. They tie people to themselves. This can lead to dependencies. 'I don't make any decisions without my master,' one woman said to me in a counselling session several years ago.

J: You are talking here about how to differentiate between an authentic and an inauthentic master. Yet Jesus gives us a clear indication: 'You will know them by their fruits' (Matthew 7:16). To be sure that we are dealing with a true master takes time and proper verification. Sometimes the fruits are not always immediately recognisable.

AC: It seems to me that Ignatius was a master at differentiating between good and bad fruit. He went through Jesus' master class. His 'discernment of the spirits' (SE 313–336) is a great gift to help understand what is going on within us spiritually, to understand the 'inner motions', as Ignatius calls them. What he describes here proves him to be a true 'master student'. Did he see himself as a student?

J: Yes. Ignatius writes in his autobiography about his personal desert time in Manresa when he went through deep spiritual processes: 'In this time God treated him in the same way as a schoolteacher treats a child when he is teaching it' (*A Pilgrim's Journey*, no. 27). When he had indeed become a master, Ignatius said that what he had learned at this time was to learn from his mistakes.

AC: That sounds good – and humble.

J: Throughout his life Ignatius understood himself to be someone who was always learning and practising. This characterises his whole view of humankind: 'Practise makes the master', as the saying goes. His Spiritual Exercises are his masterpiece and his legacy to the Church.

AC: You have been talking about the Spiritual Exercises of Ignatius. Why does he never refer to a 'retreat master' in them?

J: Thinking about the process of the retreat, I assume that for Ignatius only Jesus is the actual Master. Do you like the expression 'retreat master'?

AC: I have to smile when I think about that. On one retreat course when I was part of the accompanying team I remember being accommodated in a room with the label 'retreat master' on the door. That touched me and somehow it pleased me, too. On the other hand, I asked myself: Is this really appropriate for me? Is there not only the *one* Master whom I can assist?

J: In the annotations to his Spiritual Exercises, Ignatius speaks quite simply about 'the one who gives the spiritual exercises and the one who is to receive them' (SE 1). In sharing the experiences of the retreatant, the person who gives the retreat also becomes the receiver. This is very much my experience when I am giving retreats. I find it especially awe-inspiring when retreatants share with me the experiences that they have had whilst praying with the Name of Jesus Christ.

AC: It is not for nothing that in the hymn recorded in the Letter to the Philippians, it says that God has 'granted him the name above every name' (Philippians 2:9). Overall there are more than a hundred names or metaphors for Jesus in the New Testament. They, together with the spiritual experiences that are expressed in them, are all incorporated in the one name, Jesus, which means in Hebrew 'God saves', 'God is generous'. The Master's name is more than a label. After the end of Jesus' life on earth, the first Christians called upon his name and experienced him as being present in it.

J: Praying with the name of Jesus Christ is central to the Gries Path of contemplation. Through our doing without pictures and concepts of Jesus, we are led into a direct relationship with the Christ, present in the present moment. Retreatants are aware of this in many different ways. They often speak of an energy that physically straightens them up. Or else they experience: Here is someone who is here for me.

AC: I once experienced the power of the name myself when I was making a retreat in Haus Gries. In terms of following the process of the introductory steps, we had not yet arrived at the name. Nevertheless, during a time of prayer the name of Jesus Christ was suddenly and unexpectedly there in my prayer. I was drawn interiorly to stay with the name in my prayer. I could feel an all-encompassing presence. It was on 1 January. At mass that evening I discovered that we were celebrating the Feast of the Holy Name of Jesus. I was overjoyed because my personal experience seemed to be confirmed by this. I sometimes ask myself: If there is such a presence and effective power in the name of Jesus Christ, why do we Christians seek other people who could be spiritual masters for us?

J: Trusting the person who is sitting opposite me can be a positive and healing experience. A physical space is opened in this way in which I can share whatever I need to. An experienced spiritual companion can help me to differentiate between the different things that are going on within me and to keep me from delusions. Such a person can help me to orient myself on Jesus Christ by being focused on him themselves as well as being a channel for the Spirit of Christ working within them.

AC: We have just spoken a lot about the power and the effectiveness of the master. But the master Jesus also encounters us in a helpless and vulnerable way.

J: In Jesus, vulnerability and authority are not contradictory. Jesus shows himself to be a human being who has also suffered from being vulnerable. Nevertheless, he does not lose himself in his emotions, but rather stays focused on his Father in all things. Even at the lowest points of his life he remains trusting. In this way his vulnerability and weakness become a channel through which God's power can unfold. Whoever has accepted their own vulnerability comes to an authentic life and can also understand the vulnerability of others.

AC: This is an important point for our own spiritual journey and for the accompaniment of other people. We can only come to ourselves if we have faced our own truth and know our own strengths and weaknesses. This radiates out of us and is healing to the people whom we meet.

J: Retreatants often have a fine sensitivity as to whether or not their retreat companion has gone through this school of self-knowledge.

AC: One of Jesus' master students, Mary Magdalene, had self-knowledge. She had gone through a process of purification and illumination with Jesus. It is said that she was freed and cleansed of seven demons. She acquired a deeper knowledge of both herself and Jesus on his journeys and learned to love him. She suffered through the dying and death of her beloved Lord, sat opposite his grave and was allowed to recognise him after the resurrection. These experiences enabled her to give witness to him as 'Rabbuni', that is to say, 'my Master' (John 20:16) after the resurrection.

J: I find the word 'my' remarkable here. She can completely accept the master whom she followed before his death and whom she revered. She accepts him completely and takes him as her own: 'This is my master to whom I want to belong.' In so doing, she took a major decision for herself and for the future direction of her life.

AC: That reminds me of a man I once accompanied during a retreat. He knew the Bible well and yet Jesus the master somehow remained distant from him. Up to then he had felt little of this relationship. He expressed it with the words: 'Ultimately, Jesus has to deliver.' Jesus did 'deliver' and the decisive turnaround occurred: in prayer the retreatant was allowed to experience Jesus Christ as intimately present. From being 'the' master he became 'his' master.

J: We have been walking quite a way with each other now. It's time for us to take a moment to pause and to reflect on the effect that the conversation has had on us. Like the disciples on the road to Emmaus we want to ask ourselves:

Where were my eyes opened?
Where was my heart burning?

AC: My eyes were opened at the realisation that choosing Jesus as my master is decisive for the spiritual life. When this happens, the master Jesus Christ has arrived in my heart, tangibly.

J: My heart burned at the insight of just how strikingly the Bible portrays Jesus as a spiritual master.

Exercises:
15 minutes silence

Where were my eyes opened whilst I was reading this?
Where was my heart burning?

On whom do I orient myself in my life?

Have I found my master?

Appendix 1

Guidelines for Praying the Jesus Prayer (Gries Path) – 30 Minutes

Place

I choose a place where I have the greatest chance of not being disturbed. I prepare it to my taste, perhaps with a picture, a candle, a flower. I prepare where I will sit with whatever else I might need (e.g. suitable chair, prayer stool, meditation or other cushions, blankets).

Sitting

I choose a comfortable position, sitting upright with as much contact with the floor as possible. I need to choose a posture in which I can remain still without having to change my position for the duration of the exercise. This enables me to be fully attentive in a restful posture, with an inner stillness. I either close my eyes or else focus on a point about a metre in front of me on the floor. I do not let my eyes wander.

Jesus Prayer

I become aware of my breathing. I lay the palms of my hands together. I take time to become aware of their touching each other as well as of the space between them. Every time I exhale, I say 'Jesus'. Every time I inhale, I say 'Christ'. I pay attention to whether or not I experience an inner resonance connected with the name 'Jesus Christ', or an atmosphere into which I am drawn. How am I experiencing my relationship with Jesus Christ? I stay with every breath, breathing out 'Jesus' and breathing in 'Christ'. The name can accompany the natural rhythm of my breathing. I remain wide awake, with lively interest and fully present. Whenever I am distracted, I return to the awareness of my breathing, my hands and the name of Jesus Christ.

Appendix 2

Living Contemplatively in Daily Life

Prayer and everyday life are by no means separate worlds. What you practise in prayer will change your everyday life and in your everyday life you can practise what is important in prayer.

In your daily living, you can put into practice the Jesus Prayer, for example at those times when you are waiting, on the train, out in nature, at work. Be present to the present moment. Live in the here and now. If you are doing something, focus on that rather than being preoccupied with something that is past or something that is yet to come. Stay with your whole attention on what you are doing right now, or with the person with whom you are at this moment.

Be aware of what comes towards you from life itself. Let the whole of life touch you, even unpleasant situations. That does not mean that you should not get rid of difficulties if it is at all possible to do so. When you have no other option, however, then practise acceptance. Make yourself free from the desire to achieve results. Accept yourself as you are and be willing, time and again, to forgive.

Times of quiet and times of activity

Times of quiet and times of activity should exist alongside each other in a healthy relationship. When trying to organise your everyday life, the following five priorities, put together by Franz Jalics SJ, might be helpful:

1. Sleep
Only someone who is well rested can be wide awake in meditation and do their work in everyday life properly. When you are

looking for a way to fit your prayer time into your daily routine, do not cut short your time of sleep. Instead consider which of your activities or daily practices are unnecessary or unhelpful and could be dropped. Take care with the way you organise your evenings.

2. Body
Make sure your body has enough physical exercise. Eat healthily, using all your senses to appreciate the food. Teresa of Avila says: 'Be good to your body so that your soul wants to live in it.'

3. Prayer
A well-rested and healthy body can pray better, therefore prayer is in third place. For many people, the best time for prayer is in the morning, before our duties make their demands on us. In this way, our day immediately has a spiritual orientation.

4. People around us
Time for family, friends etc. does not have to be long. However, give others your full attention when you are there. Give your time freely. Be there without any preconceived intention and be fully present.

5. Work
Other priorities should not be neglected because of the demands of work. That means, for example, that you should not shorten your time of prayer because of work. When you are at work, be fully attentive to it.

Aids to keep going

Contemplation groups
It could be helpful to be part of a prayer group that meets regularly (see Contact Details, p.96), having contact with like-minded people and sharing with them.

Contemplative retreats
In order to deepen our contemplative prayer it can be helpful to go on a retreat each year. Here several days are spent in silence and devoted to intensive prayer. They are a special school of awareness and intensive times of orientation, without the disturbances of our everyday lives (see Contact Details, p.96).

Spiritual accompaniment
You can choose a trustworthy person who is experienced in prayer and with whom you can have regular conversations about your prayer life and prayer experience. These conversations would normally take place once every four weeks. If you keep a spiritual journal, the entries can be a good basis for reflecting on your prayer life and may be helpful for the conversation.

Personal spiritual 'rule'
It can be helpful for you to note down some of the important cornerstones of your spiritual life. This creates commitment. Your daily practice can keep being oriented on this 'rule'. The rule must be realistic, feasible and specific. It should include important points regarding your way of living, your spiritual life, your relationships, your daily routine, your work, all of which can be more precisely formulated in it. The rule can be modified and reformulated, as necessary, to fit in with changing circumstances and developments in your life.

Suggestions for prayer

Weekly participation in a religious service, a Eucharist or Communion service can deepen our personal prayer – and vice versa. Sometimes, if you are particularly stressed, you might find it difficult to quieten yourself. Then it might be helpful, before you start to meditate, to go for a short walk, or to do some body-awareness exercises or some breathing exercises, or simply to allow yourself a time of peace and quiet.

Try to find a regular time for your prayer. This will help it to become safeguarded in your daily routine. The guidelines given for praying the Jesus Prayer (see Appendix 1, p.92) might be a helpful model for your time of prayer in daily life.

Contact Details

In most of the retreats in Haus Gries accompaniment in English is possible. We also offer online retreats in English. Information about the Gries Path and registration for contemplative retreats: www.haus-gries.de

The standard book of the Gries Path by Fr Franz Jalics SJ has been published in two English translations:

> *Contemplative Retreat: An Introduction to a Contemplative Way of Life and to the Jesus Prayer*, Maitland, FL: Xulon Press, 2003
> *Called to Share in HIS Life: Introduction to a Contemplative Way of Life and the Jesus Prayer (a Retreat)*, Trans. Sr Lucia Wiedenhöver OCD, Mumbai: St Pauls, 2002

UK Contact

Sr Mary Dargie: St Augustine's Priory, Old Colwyn, LL29 95W, enquiries@houseofprayer.org.uk
Paddy Rylands: 14 Morfa Rd, Llandudno, LL30 2BS, paddyrylands@gmail.com